P9-CEY-583

allergy friendly food

The essential guide to avoiding allergies,
additives and problem chemicals

Dr. Anne R Swain, Dr. Velencia L Soutter
and Dr. Robert H Loblay
from
Royal Prince Alfred Hospital
Allergy Unit

BARNES & NOBLE BOOKS

NEW YORK

contents

With comprehensive and easy-to-use food charts, sensible nutrition advice and lots of helpful lifestyle tips, this chapter contains all the information you'll need to get the most out of *Allergy Friendly Food*. Take the time to read it through—leading allergy experts explain the difference between food intolerance and allergy, what food chemicals are, how they affect us, and how best to adjust our daily life and diet in order to avoid them.

food allergies
& intolerances

understanding and managing food allergies and intolerances

For most of us, food is more than a daily necessity. We get personal pleasure from it. We nurture our children with it. And sharing it around the table is at the heart of our family and social life. For some people, though, foods can cause distressing, even dangerous, reactions, or chronic ill health, and that's why we've written this book.

Foods can upset people for many reasons. This book will help you understand more about the different kinds of reaction that can occur—food intolerance, food allergy and celiac disease—and the various foods and food substances that can trigger them. Based on more than 20 years of experience and research at the Allergy Unit at Royal Prince Alfred Hospital and the University of Sydney, we've developed a comprehensive dietary testing and management program now in use throughout Australia for people with food reactions.

Having a food problem may restrict your food choices somewhat, but it doesn't mean you can't enjoy eating and sharing with family and friends. In this book we've provided a range of recipes for all occasions, helpful hints for food preparation, and lifestyle advice to help people living with a food problem stay well and enjoy a full and rich life.

Even if you don't have a food problem yourself, you probably have a friend or relative who does. We hope this book will provide an opportunity for everyone to learn more about 'friendly' food.

understanding food intolerance

Understanding the difference between intolerance and other types of food reaction is an important starting point because the approach to dealing with them is quite different. Unlike allergies and celiac disease, which are immune reactions to food proteins, intolerances don't involve the immune system at all. They are triggered by food chemicals which cause reactions by irritating nerve endings in different parts of the body, rather in the way that certain drugs can cause side-effects in sensitive people.

The chemicals involved in food intolerances are found in many different foods, so the approach involves identifying them and reducing your intake of *groups of foods*, all of which contain the same offending substances. By contrast, protein allergens are unique to each food (for example, egg, milk and peanut), and dealing with a food allergy involves identifying and avoiding all traces of *that particular food*. Similarly, gluten, the protein involved in celiac disease, is only found in certain grains (wheat, barley, rye) and their elimination is the basis of a gluten-free diet.

natural food chemicals Chemicals are found everywhere in nature, including in foods. Some are beneficial; for example, the vitamins we need for good health, and the flavor and aroma substances that make foods so enjoyable. On the other hand, many plants contain substances which are poisonous to humans, and of course we avoid cultivating these as foods. The staple foods we eat today have been selected by trial and error over thousands of years, both for their nutritional value and because most people can tolerate them without getting sick.

Some people are born with a sensitive constitution and react more readily to food chemicals than others. The tendency is probably inherited, but environmental triggers—a sudden change of diet, a bad food or drug reaction, a nasty viral infection (for example, gastroenteritis, glandular fever)—can bring on symptoms at any age by altering the way the body reacts to food chemicals. Women often become more sensitive in their child-bearing years, perhaps due to hormonal changes, which might be nature's way of preventing pregnant and breast-feeding women from eating foods that could harm a developing baby.

Babies are more vulnerable to food chemicals because their metabolism, gastrointestinal and nervous systems are immature, which is why they often prefer bland foods. As children mature, their bodies become accustomed to handling small amounts of rich, spicy and highly flavored foods, which usually only cause ill effects if eaten in excess.

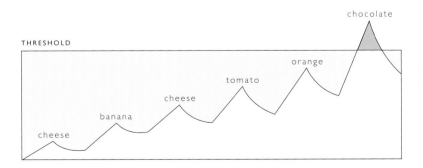

THRESHOLD

chocolate

orange

tomato

cheese

banana

cheese

cheese

Chemical threshold The small amounts of natural chemicals present in a particular food may not be enough to cause a reaction right away. However, because one substance may be common to many different foods it can accumulate in the body, causing a reaction when the threshold is finally exceeded. On this graph, all the foods shown contain natural amines. Although the last food eaten (chocolate) is often blamed for a reaction, all the others have contributed as well.

It's important to realize that the natural chemicals in many 'healthy' foods can be just as much of a problem for sensitive people as the 'artificial' ones used as food additives. Foods vary tremendously in chemical composition. The natural substances most likely to upset sensitive individuals—salicylates, amines and glutamate—are the ones common to many different foods, and therefore consumed in greatest quantity in the daily diet. As a rule, the tastier a food is, the richer it's likely to be in natural chemicals. A comprehensive list of foods and their natural chemical content is shown in the charts on pages 16–21.

food additives People who are sensitive to natural food chemicals are usually also sensitive to one or more of the common food additives such as preservatives, artificial colors and flavorings. Reactions to these can be easier to recognize than reactions to natural chemicals because of the higher doses present in processed foods. As with the natural chemicals, individuals vary in their sensitivity to particular additives, and it's often worthwhile testing this out systematically rather than avoiding all additives. The ones most likely to be a problem in people with food intolerance are listed on page 244 along with their code numbers.

food intolerance reactions Symptoms triggered by food chemical intolerances vary from person to person. The commonest ones are recurrent hives and swellings, headaches, sinus trouble, mouth ulcers, nausea, stomach pains and bowel irritation. Some people feel vaguely unwell, with flu-like aches and pains, or get unusually tired, run-down or moody, often for no apparent reason. Children can become irritable and restless, and behavioral problems can be aggravated in those with nervous system disorders such as ADHD (attention deficit hyperactivity disorder). Even

Dose dependence Food intolerance reactions are dose dependent. A small amount of a chemical-rich food (e.g. one or two strawberries; a slice of fresh tomato) may cause no symptoms, whereas a larger amount that exceeds your dose threshold (e.g. a whole bowl of strawberries; tomato concentrated as a sauce or paste) can provoke a reaction. Eating small amounts regularly can cause a gradual build-up with symptoms developing after a few days.

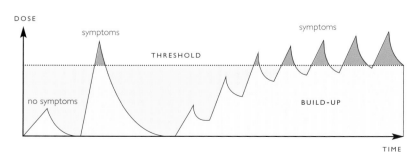

breast-fed babies can have food intolerance reactions due to chemicals from the mother's diet getting into the breast milk, causing colicky irritable behavior, loose stools, eczema and diaper rashes.

dealing with food intolerances People vary in their degree of sensitivity to food chemicals, and whether or not they get symptoms depends on the dose ingested. If you're not too sensitive (with a high dose threshold) you may only react after a particularly rich meal or after bingeing on highly preserved/flavored/colored foods. Avoiding these may be all you need to do to stay well.

However, if you're at the other end of the spectrum (with a low dose threshold) you may develop symptoms over several days or weeks from the cumulative effects of small amounts of natural chemicals. Because these are present in many otherwise 'healthy' foods in a normal diet, you'll have to be much more careful with what you eat on a daily basis.

The hints in this book may be enough to get you on the right track, but before making any major change to your diet, go and see your doctor. Food intolerances can be distressing, but they don't cause permanent damage to the body. If you have persistent symptoms it's a good idea to first make sure some serious disease hasn't been overlooked.

If you're having trouble working out which foods are upsetting you, professional help may be needed to investigate the problem more systematically. The first step is to follow a strict elimination diet for 3 or 4 weeks to see if symptoms disappear. You may get a withdrawal effect in the first week or so (with a temporary flare-up of symptoms for a few days) so don't give up too soon. Once your symptoms have settled and you're feeling better for at least 7 days in a row, you're ready to start doing challenge tests to find out which chemicals in your diet cause reactions.

Challenge tests can either be done double-blind (with purified food chemicals taken in capsules), or with carefully selected foods each containing only one problem substance. Once your problem substances have been identified, a dietitian with experience in the field can advise you how to manage your diet using the *Allergy Friendly Food* charts on pages 16–21.

Don't be discouraged—food intolerances needn't be permanent. You may well be able to build up your tolerance level by gradually increasing the amount and variety of 'low' and 'moderate' foods over several weeks or months, and eventually return to a more normal diet. Even if this is not possible, you'll learn ways of avoiding severe reactions by looking out for the foods that upset you most.

DIAGNOSIS OF FOOD INTOLERANCE

There are no reliable skin or blood tests for diagnosis of food intolerances. Food intolerances are diagnosed by a dietary elimination and challenge test process.

COMMON FOOD ALLERGENS

- *Peanut and other nuts*
- *Egg*
- *Milk*
- *Seafood*
- *Sesame*
- *Wheat*
- *Soy*

understanding food allergies

Allergies occur when an overactive immune system produces proteins called IgE antibodies against substances in the environment that are otherwise harmless—pollen, house dust mites, molds, animal hair (dander), and in some cases, specific food proteins. Food allergy is mainly a problem of infants, toddlers and young children. Over 90% of cases are associated with atopic eczema—an intensely itchy chronic skin rash affecting the face, arms, legs, and other parts of the body—and there is usually a family history of allergic disorders, such as asthma, hay fever and eczema.

In adults, a single food such as peanut or shellfish is usually involved, but children are commonly allergic to two or three foods, sometimes more. The most common ones are peanut, egg, milk, other nuts, seafoods and/or sesame. Fortunately, most children grow out of their egg and milk allergies before they reach school age, or during the early school years, but allergies to nuts and seafoods can persist. Wheat and soy can cause allergies, but they tend to be mild and transient.

New food allergies can occasionally arise in adult life, usually with crustaceans and other more exotic foods that are not eaten in childhood. With rare exceptions, reactions to fruits, vegetables, herbs and spices are due to chemical intolerances rather than allergies. Skin prick tests or blood tests (radioallergosorbent test or RAST) can detect IgE antibodies in people with allergies, but are of no value for diagnosis of intolerances.

food allergy reactions Food allergy reactions vary in severity, depending on how sensitive the person is and how much of the food they've eaten. Mild reactions may only cause a little eczema or a few hives, and the cause may not be obvious. More severe reactions are usually obvious and occur consistently, every time the person has the food. Contact with the mouth and tongue can cause an immediate burning sensation, with hives and redness around the face and, if the food is swallowed, an immediate feeling of being unwell can be followed by vomiting, cramps and diarrhea. The face, mouth and eyes can swell dramatically, and hives on the body can join into large, rapidly spreading welts.

The most severe type of reaction—anaphylaxis—can progress rapidly with breathing difficulty (from swelling of the throat or severe asthma), allergic shock and collapse, and can be life-threatening if not treated immediately with adrenaline (epinephrine) by injection. In the most sensitive people with a food allergy, tiny amounts of the food (pin-head sized) can be enough to provoke a severe reaction.

celiac disease

Celiac disease is caused by an immune reaction to gluten, a protein found in wheat, barley and rye. The reaction causes inflammation and damage to the lining of the small bowel, which impairs its ability to absorb nutrients. Typical symptoms include mouth ulcers, fatigue, bloating, cramps and diarrhea, but some people have no symptoms at all, and in others the only clue may be anaemia (due to iron or folic acid deficiency) or an unusual chronic skin rash (dermatitis herpetiformis). Celiac disease should not be confused with wheat allergy, which rarely occurs beyond infancy, or the stomach and bowel irritation that gluten can sometimes cause in people with chemical intolerances.

Screening blood tests are available, but definite diagnosis requires a small bowel biopsy. These tests can become negative after a few weeks of gluten avoidance, so it's best to get checked before you go on a gluten-free diet if you think there's a possibility you might have celiac disease.

Untreated celiac disease carries a long-term risk of nutritional deficiency, osteoporosis and/or bowel malignancy. Currently, a life-long gluten-free diet is the only known treatment.

SOURCES OF GLUTEN				
NONE POSSIBLE	NONE DETECTABLE *	TRACE AMOUNTS *	MINOR SOURCES	MAJOR SOURCES
Arrowroot	Caramel color	Dextrin (postage stamp adhesive)	Cornstarch/cornflour	Barley
Buckwheat	Dextrose	Maltodextrin	Malt	Bran
Corn/Maize	Glucose	Pre-gel starch	Malt extract	Cookies
Lupin	Glucose powder	Thickeners (1400–1450)	Malt vinegar	Couscous
Maize cornstarch/ cornflour	Glucose syrup		Modified starch	Crackers
Millet			Oatmeal	Flour
Modified maize starch			Oats	Noodles
Polenta			Starch	Pasta
Psyllium			Wheaten cornstarch/ cornflour	Rye
Rice			Wheat starch	Semolina
Sago				Spelt
Seeds				Triticale
Sorghum				Wheat
Soy				Wheat bran
Tapioca				Wheat flour
Wine vinegar				Wheat germ
				Wheatmeal

* In foods/ingredients derived from wheat. Check label on package.

good nutrition on a low chemical diet

If you are on a long-term restricted diet because of food intolerances, you'll need to pay careful attention to maintaining good nutrition.

Protein, fat and carbohydrates come from staple foods. Proteins provide the building blocks for your tissues. Fats and carbohydrates supply the fuel for your body to generate and store energy. Even on a low-chemical diet you should be able to meet your protein and energy needs. If you begin losing weight, you're probably not getting enough calories (kilojoules) and need to increase your intake of staple foods. Ask your dietitian for help if necessary.

Vitamins and minerals are necessary in small amounts for your metabolism to function normally. Remember that energy comes from major nutrients, not vitamins, so if you feel tired and run-down more vitamins are not likely to be the answer.

If your diet is highly restricted, ask your dietitian to check whether you are meeting your daily requirements. If in doubt, you should take a suitable multivitamin and calcium supplement (see the Shopping List on page 242).

LOW CHEMICAL SOURCES OF MAJOR NUTRIENTS

NUTRIENT	FOOD SOURCES
Protein	meats, fish, poultry, eggs, dairy foods
Fat	oils, margarine, meat, eggs, dairy foods
Carbohydrates	rice, potato, bread, pasta, cereals, white sugar
Fiber	wholegrain cereals, wholegrain bread, cabbage, Brussels sprouts, lentils, beans, pears
Essential fatty acids (omega-3 fats)	canola, sunflower and safflower oils and margarine, flaxseed oil, egg yolk
Natural antioxidants	foods containing vitamins A and C (below) and vitamin E (canola, sunflower and safflower oils and margarine)
Vitamin A	dairy foods, eggs, margarine, fish, lettuce, Brussels sprouts, beans, cabbage
Vitamin B1	breads (brown and white), brown rice, whole wheat pasta, fortified breakfast cereals
Vitamin B12	meat, chicken, fish, eggs, milk
Other B vitamins	dairy products, meat, chicken, fish, lentils, wholegrain cereals
Vitamin C	potato, parsley, Brussels sprouts, cabbage, peas, rutabaga (swedes)
Folic acid	Brussels sprouts, lettuce, cabbage, lentils, pulses, wholegrain cereals, fortified breakfast cereals
Iron	meat, chicken, fish, eggs, lentils, wholegrain cereals
Calcium	dairy foods, calcium fortified soy products

Salt intake is significantly reduced when processed foods are eliminated, so table salt can safely be used to add flavor to meals on a low chemical diet.

Cholesterol intake is reduced by cutting out processed foods. It can be further reduced by trimming the fat off meats, discarding chicken skin, and using low-fat milk. Use polyunsaturated oils and margarines where possible.

Vegetarians need to choose suitable alternatives to provide the necessary proteins. Suitable low-chemical legumes include lentils, chickpeas, soy and kidney beans. Combining these with dairy foods, cereals and/or nuts and seeds will provide all the essential amino acids.

Pregnancy and breast-feeding will increase your requirements for calories, iron, folic acid and calcium. See your dietitian for detailed advice.

common misconceptions

Popular diets come and go, based on whatever alternative theories are currently in fashion; for example, hypoglycemia, food family rotation, Candida, leaky gut and liver detoxification. These diets generally eliminate all additives and a wide range of foods that are rich in natural chemicals, so it's not surprising that people with food intolerance who follow these diets often feel better, at least temporarily.

This is also true of so-called 'yeast-free', 'wheat-free' and 'sugar-free' diets. If your health improves on one of these diets, it's easy to jump to the mistaken conclusion that yeast, wheat or sugar must have been the culprit. If you find that sweet foods, such as cakes, honey, jam and chocolate, upset you, it's likely to be due to the natural chemicals and/or additives in them rather than the sugar. In fact, white (refined) sugar is perfectly safe for sensitive individuals, because any natural chemicals that might cause reactions have been removed in the refining process.

There is a common belief that dairy products are bad for people with 'allergies'. In fact, this is not usually so. If you feel better avoiding dairy it may be because you've cut out the natural amines in Cheddar cheeses and chocolates, or the flavorings in yogurt, ice cream and milk shakes. Milk or wheat can sometimes irritate the stomach and bowels in people with food intolerance, but this will often settle down after the relevant food chemicals have been identified and eliminated for a few weeks.

Lactose intolerance is a genetic difficulty in digesting lactose, and can cause bowel symptoms. However, it's not usually necessary to exclude all dairy products, as most people with lactose intolerance can tolerate small quantities of milk and yogurt. If you react to cheese (which contains no lactose) you're likely to have intolerance to food chemicals other than lactose.

Once you know which foods you can tolerate safely, apply these general principles:

VARY the foods you eat from day to day as much as possible

EAT MOST bread, rice, potato, and other cereals, fruit and vegetables

EAT MODERATELY meat, fish, chicken, dairy or soy products (or vegetarian alternatives)

EAT LEAST fats and oils

DRINK MOSTLY water

MAINTAIN a steady, acceptable weight

understanding the food chemical charts

The foods in the charts on the following pages are listed in columns and shaded according to their overall content of natural chemicals, taking into account the amounts you'd normally eat in a day. Foods with the strongest flavor and aroma are more likely to cause problems because they have the highest content of natural chemicals.

Low foods are almost never a problem.
Moderate and high foods may upset you, depending on how sensitive you are and how much you eat.
Very high foods often cause symptoms in sensitive people.

SALICYLATES ⓢ are a family of natural plant chemicals found in many fruits, vegetables, herbs, spices and nuts as well as in most honeys, jams, yeast extracts, teas, coffees, juices, beers and wines. Levels are high in unripe fruit,

FOOD CHEMICALS IN VEGETABLES

LOW	MODERATE	HIGH	VERY HIGH
Bamboo shoots	ⓢ Asparagus	ⓢ Alfalfa	S+A Avocado
Brussels sprouts	ⓢ Beetroot	ⓢ Artichoke	S+A Cauliflower
Cabbage	ⓢ Butternut squash	ⓢ Belgian endive	S+A Eggplant
Celery	(pumpkin)	(witlof)	(aubergine)
Chives	ⓢ Carrot	ⓢ Chicory	S+A Fava (broad)
Choko	ⓢ Chinese vegetables	ⓢ Chilli	bean
Dried beans	ⓢ Lettuce (other)	ⓢ Corn	S+A Gherkin
Dried peas	ⓢ Marrow	ⓢ Cucumber	S+A Olive
Leeks	ⓢ Parsnip	ⓢ Onion	ⓖ S+A Broccoli
Lentils	ⓢ Potato (new, red)	ⓢ Pepper (capsicum)	ⓖ S+A Champignon
Lettuce (Iceberg)	ⓢ Snow peas	ⓢ Pumpkin (other)	ⓖ S+A English spinach
Mungbean sprouts	(mangetout)	ⓢ Radish	ⓖ S+A Mushroom
Parsley	ⓢ Snow pea	ⓢ Water chestnut	ⓖ S+A Swiss chard
Potato (white, peeled)	(mangetout) sprouts	ⓢ Watercress	(silverbeet)
Red cabbage	ⓢ Sweet potato	ⓢ Zucchini (courgette)	ⓖ S+A Tomato
Rutabaga (swede)	ⓢ Turnip		
Shallots	ⓖ ⓢ Green peas		

ⓢ *Salicylates*   S+A *Both Salicylates and Amines*   ⓖ *Also Glutamate (MSG)*

and decrease with ripening. Salicylates are also present in flavorings (for example, peppermint), perfumes, scented toiletries, eucalyptus oils and some medications (aspirin is a member of the salicylate family).

AMINES Ⓐ come from protein breakdown or fermentation. Large amounts are present in cheese, chocolate, wines, beer, yeast extracts and fish products. They are also present in certain fruits and vegetables (for example, banana, avocado and tomato) and the levels increase as the fruit ripens.

GLUTAMATE(MSG) Ⓖ is an amino acid—a building block of all proteins—and is present naturally in most foods. In its free form, not linked to protein, it enhances the flavor of food. This is why foods rich in glutamate (for example, tomato, cheese, bouillon cubes, sauces, meat and yeast extracts) are used in many meals. Pure monosodium glutamate (MSG) can also be used as an additive to increase the flavor of soups, sauces, Asian cooking and snack foods.

Many plant foods have high levels of natural pesticides and preservatives in the skin or outer leaves. 'Organically' grown fruits and vegetables can have even higher levels. Peel fruit and vegetables thickly or discard the outer leaves.

FOOD CHEMICALS IN FRUIT

LOW	MODERATE	HIGH	VERY HIGH
Pear (ripe, peeled)	Ⓢ Apple (Golden, Red Delicious)	Ⓢ Apple (Jonathan, Granny Smith)	S+A Avocado
Pear (canned, in sugar syrup)	Ⓢ Cherimoya (custard apple)	Ⓢ Apricot	S+A Date
	Ⓢ Loquat	Ⓢ Berries	S+A Grapefruit
	Ⓢ Mango	Ⓢ Blackcurrant	S+A Kiwi fruit
	Ⓢ Pear (unripe, unpeeled)	Ⓢ Cantaloupe (rockmelon)	S+A Mandarin
	Ⓢ Pear (canned, in juice)	Ⓢ Cherry	S+A Orange
	Ⓢ Persimmon	Ⓢ Guava	S+A Passionfruit
	Ⓢ Rhubarb	Ⓢ Lychee	S+A Pineapple
	Ⓢ Tamarillo	Ⓢ Nectarine	S+A Raspberry
	Ⓐ Banana	Ⓢ Peach	S+A Tangelo
	Ⓐ Papaya	Ⓢ Pomegranate	Ⓖ S+A Grape
		Ⓢ Redcurrant	Ⓖ S+A Plum
		Ⓢ Strawberry	Ⓖ S+A Prune
		Ⓢ Watermelon	Ⓖ S+A Raisin
		S+A Fig	Ⓖ S+A Tomato
		S+A Lemon	
		S+A Sugar banana	

Ⓢ *Salicylates* Ⓐ *Amines* S+A *Both Salicylates and Amines* Ⓖ *Also Glutamate (MSG)*

FOOD CHEMICALS IN MEATS, CHICKEN, FISH & EGGS

LOW	HIGH	VERY HIGH
Beef Chicken (no skin) Eggs Fish (fresh, white) Lamb Rabbit Sausage casing Veal	Ⓐ Aged meat Ⓐ Bacon Ⓐ Chicken liver Ⓐ Chicken skin Ⓐ Frozen fish Ⓐ Gravy (meat juice) Ⓐ Ham Ⓐ Pork Ⓐ Salmon Ⓐ Sardines Ⓐ Tuna	Ⓐ Anchovies Ⓐ Fish roe Ⓐ Fish (dried, pickled, salted, smoked) Ⓐ Offal Ⓐ Smoked meat and chicken Ⓐ Tuna (canned) Ⓖ S+A Meat pies Ⓖ S+A Processed luncheon meat Ⓖ S+A Salami Ⓖ S+A Sausages Ⓖ S+A Seasoned meats and chicken

Ⓐ *Amines*   S+A *Both Salicylates and Amines*   Ⓖ *Also Glutamate (MSG)*

Fresh meats, poultry, seafoods, eggs, dairy and soy are all low in natural chemicals. However, amines and glutamate form as a result of protein breakdown during cooking and the ageing process. Eat fresh products, or freeze and consume within 4 weeks.

FOOD CHEMICALS IN DAIRY FOODS & SOY PRODUCTS

LOW	HIGH	VERY HIGH
Dairy Food Cream Fresh cheese (e.g. ricotta) Milk (cow, goat) Plain wholemilk yogurt	Ⓐ Mild cheese	Ⓖ Ⓐ Cheddar cheeses (all)
Soy Products Soy milk Soy yogurt Tofu		Ⓖ Ⓐ Miso Ⓖ Ⓐ Soy sauce Ⓖ Ⓐ Tempeh

Ⓐ *Amines*   Ⓖ *Also Glutamate (MSG)*

FOOD CHEMICALS IN DRINKS

LOW	MODERATE	HIGH	VERY HIGH
Carob powder	S Coffee	S Fruit juices (all)	S Fruit flavored drinks
Milk (cow, goat)	S Coffee substitutes		A Chocolate flavored drinks
Soy milk	S Tea (decaffeinated; herbal, except peppermint)		A Cocoa powder
Lemon lime soda (sparkling clear lemonade) (unpreserved)	S Tea substitutes		S+A Cola drinks
			S+A Cordials/fruit mixes
Rice milk			S+A Orange juice
			S+A Sodas/soft drinks
Coffee (decaffeinated)			G S+A Tomato juice
			G S+A Vegetable juice
Gin			
Vodka			S Tea
Whisky			S Peppermint tea
			S+A Beer
			S+A Cider
			G S+A Brandy, Port, Rum and Sherry
			G S+A Liqueurs
			G S+A Wine

S *Salicylates*   A *Amines*   S+A *Both Salicylates and Amines*   G *Also Glutamate (MSG)*

FOOD CHEMICALS IN JAMS, SPREADS, SUGARS & SWEETS

LOW	MODERATE	VERY HIGH
Caramels	S Molasses	S Chewing gum
Carob	S Raw sugar	S Honey
Golden syrup		S Jams (all)
Malt extract		S Liquorice
Maple syrup		S Mint-flavored sweets
Marshmallow (white)		S Peppermints
Rice syrup		A Chocolate (all)
Sugar		A Cocoa
Toffee		S+A Fruit-flavored sweets and ices
		S+A Lemon curd (butter)

S *Salicylates*   A *Amines*   S+A *Both Salicylates and Amines*

FOOD CHEMICALS IN CEREALS, GRAINS & FLOURS

LOW	HIGH
Arrowroot	S Corn cereals
Barley	S Cornmeal
Buckwheat	S Polenta
Cornstarch (cornflour)	S Breakfast cereals with honey
Malt	A Breakfast cereals with cocoa
Rice	S+A Breakfast cereals with fruit, nuts and coconut
Rice cereals (plain)	
Rice flour	
Rolled oats	
Sago	
Soy flour	
Rye flour	
Wheat	
Wheat cereals (plain)	
Wheat flour	

S *Salicylates*   A *Amines*   S+A *Both Salicylates and Amines*

Refined rice products and wheaten cornstarch (cornflour) are the lowest in natural chemicals, though some people prefer wholegrain and whole wheat products. Try them both to see which suits you best.

FOOD CHEMICALS IN NUTS, SNACKS & CHIPS

LOW	MODERATE	HIGH	VERY HIGH
Cashews (raw)	S Corn chips (crisps)	S+A Coconut	S Honey flavors
Plain potato chips (crisps)	S Tacos	S+A Peanuts and all other nuts	G S Spicy flavors
		S+A Sesame seeds	A Almonds
		S+A Sunflower seeds	A Fruit flavors
			A Muesli bars
			G S+A Cheese flavors

S *Salicylates*   A *Amines*   S+A *Both Salicylates and Amines*   G *Also Glutamate (MSG)*

Packaged snack foods often contain preservatives such as antioxidants. 'Natural flavors' are usually high in salicylates, amines and/or glutamate. Check all labels carefully.

FOOD CHEMICALS IN FATS & OILS

LOW	MODERATE	VERY HIGH
Butter Canola oil (no antioxidant) Ghee Margarine (unpreserved, no antioxidant) Safflower oil (no antioxidant) Soy oil (no antioxidant) Sunflower oil (no antioxidant)	S Almond oil S Corn oil S Peanut oil	S+A Coconut oil S+A Olive oil S+A Sesame oil S+A Walnut oil S+A White vegetable shortening

S *Salicylates* S+A *Both Salicylates and Amines*

Margarines and oils may be preserved to stop them going rancid. Cold-pressed oils are not preserved, but retain some of the natural chemical content of the fruit or seed of origin. Oils (e.g. peanut, nut and sesame) may contain traces of allergen.

FOOD CHEMICALS IN HERBS, SPICES & CONDIMENTS

LOW	MODERATE	HIGH	VERY HIGH
Chives (as a garnish) Garlic Parsley (as a garnish) Poppy seeds Saffron Scallions (spring onions) Sea salt Vanilla	A Malt vinegar	S All other herbs and spices	G A Hydrolyzed vegetable protein G A Meat extracts G A Soy paste G A Soy sauce S+A Tandoori S+A Vinegar (cider, red and white wine) G S+A Bouillon cubes G S+A Gravies G S+A Pastes (fish, meat, tomato) G S+A Sauces (all) G S+A Tomato ketchup (sauce) G S+A Yeast extracts

S *Salicylates* A *Amines* S+A *Both Salicylates and Amines* G *Also Glutamate (MSG)*

living with food intolerances

a balancing act Food intolerance reactions can be unpleasant and inconvenient, but they are rarely serious and, as far as we know, they cause no long-term harm. Their severity depends on the amount of the offending foods you've eaten, your degree of sensitivity, and the nature of your symptoms. Once you've worked out what your problem foods are, you'll be able to decide how to balance the benefits of being free from distressing symptoms against the inconvenience of restricting your dietary choices.

eating out and social occasions People with food intolerances often have problems when dining out, but you'll be able to minimize the severity of any reaction by ordering wisely, eating small portions, and being extra careful with what you eat for a few days afterwards.

If you're planning to go out for a meal, choose a restaurant that offers some plain, simple dishes. Even if the menu doesn't have suitable choices, you can call beforehand to ask whether a special meal can be prepared for you from your tolerated ingredients or foods. This will also save you the embarrassment of having to ask detailed questions about various dishes on the menu in front of your friends and acquaintances.

If you often dine at the home of close friends or relatives who know you've got food intolerances, you can give them a copy of *Allergy Friendly Food* and let them know which recipes you prefer. Beware, though—well meaning hosts will sometimes be tempted to spice up a meal, mistakenly believing you'll enjoy it more if it has some extra flavor.

At dinner parties, where you don't wish to offend the host by asking about all the ingredients and refusing what's being offered, you can simply eat the meat and plain vegetables but leave the gravies, sauces and rich desserts. Wherever you're planning to go, it sometimes helps to take the edge off your appetite in advance by having a snack before you leave. Then you'll be less tempted to eat rich, tasty foods and suffer the consequences.

For drinking when you're out, mineral water or plain water are the safest options if you're food sensitive. If you want alcohol, choose whisky, gin or vodka (straight, or with ice, water, soda or tonic). Less sensitive individuals can often tolerate half a glass of wine. High quality wines are less likely to cause reactions—a good excuse to choose a more expensive bottle.

packing or buying lunch Stick to fresh rolls, unpreserved bread or plain crackers. For fillings, choose foods you know are safe, such as chicken, roast beef or lamb, egg, lettuce, celery, chives, bean sprouts, pear jam and golden syrup. If you're not too sensitive, you may be able to tolerate a thin slice of fresh tomato, mild cheese, beetroot, grated carrot or asparagus.

travel Plan your trip carefully. When going by road, pack suitable foods in a portable cooler, book your overnight accommodation and order your meals in advance. For long flights, take your own snacks, and avoid eating airline meals unless specially prepared. Pack enough food to last you for the first day at your destination, giving you time to find your way around, and try to book accommodation that has facilities for cooking your own food.

smells & fumes Some people with food intolerances find that their sense of smell gets more acute on a restricted diet. Strong perfume, car exhaust, gas fumes, fresh paint, cigarette smoke and other irritant smells and fumes may make you feel ill or give you a headache. Reactions like this can be unpleasant, but are not dangerous and usually resolve quickly after exposure ceases. Predictable exposures such as the perfume section in department stores, supermarket aisles with cleaning products, gas stations and underground car parks are easily avoided. If you're unexpectedly exposed, don't hang around—leave the area quickly and get some fresh air.

toiletries, cosmetics and cleaning agents Strong peppermint and menthol flavors and aromas are derived from natural salicylates, so clean your teeth with unflavored toothpaste, salt, or baking soda (bicarbonate of soda), and avoid mouthwashes. If you react to preservatives, read the labels of products carefully—most liquid cosmetics and sunscreens are preserved. If you're smell-sensitive, be careful with perfumes, deodorants, scented soaps, shampoos, conditioners, hair sprays, after-shave lotions and other toiletries. Vinegar and baking soda (bicarbonate of soda) are alternatives to strong-smelling detergents and cleaning agents.

home environment Indoor air can become quite polluted with volatile chemicals released from carpets and underlays, chipboard and other furnishing materials, cooking odors and cigarette smoke. Make sure your home is well ventilated with fresh air. Avoid using products with a strong aroma, such as air fresheners, concentrated detergents, perfumed candles, incense, eucalyptus oil, and massage and aromatherapy oils. If you feel unwell in your home environment and you're not sure why, check for hidden damp or mold, gas leaks and other sources of irritant smells or fumes.

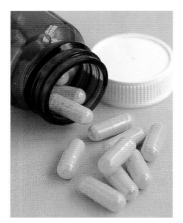

If you're planning to paint or renovate your home, and you're smell-sensitive, choose your materials carefully. Watch out for oil-based paints, glues, floor varnishes, chipboard and treated wood, all of which can emit volatile chemicals for quite some time when fresh or new. It's best not to handle these materials yourself, and you may even consider staying somewhere else for a few days or weeks while the work is being done, and airing out your home before going back. If you're not sure about a particular material or product, ask for a sample, take it home and see what happens after you've had it in your bedroom or living room for a few days.

medications   People with food intolerances often react adversely to medicines. It's best only to take essential medications prescribed by your doctor. If you're salicylate sensitive, anti-inflammatory drugs and aspirin-containing pain killers should be avoided—paracetamol and codeine are suitable alternatives in most cases.

The coloring agents used in tablets and capsules can be a problem for people who are sensitive to food colorings. If there are no suitable white alternatives, surface colorings can be washed off tablets (by rubbing them gently under running tap water) and capsules can be opened, emptied onto a spoon and taken with some maple syrup or golden syrup.

Antibiotics are of no benefit against viruses and should only be taken for bacterial infections—if your doctor is uncertain, a swab can be taken and cultured before you start any treatment.

Dental anaesthetic injections usually contain preservatives and can sometimes cause unpleasant reactions. If this happens, ask your dentist to use plain lignocaine. For major surgical procedures, general anaesthetics are rarely a problem but the premedications and post-operative pain killers can cause distressing side effects. Discuss the choice of medications with your anaesthetist beforehand.

Many antacids and children's syrups are colored, flavored and/or preserved. Check with your doctor to find suitable alternatives if necessary. Cough syrups, throat lozenges, menthol, oil of wintergreen, eucalyptus oil, liniments, massage oils, essential oils and most herbal remedies contain natural salicylates or closely related substances which frequently cause reactions in people with food intolerances, and should be avoided. If you've got a sore throat, gargle with warm salt water. If you need them, over-the-counter cold and flu preparations (with paracetamol, codeine and antihistamines) and nose sprays (with pseudoephedrine) are generally well tolerated if used as directed. Make sure you see your doctor if symptoms persist.

how to use the recipes in this book

chemical content For ease of use we've graded the recipes according to their content of the natural chemicals that can cause reactions.

> **Low chemical** recipes have been developed using ingredients from the 'low' columns in the charts on pages 16–21. They should suit you even if you're very sensitive to natural salicylates, amines and/or glutamate.

> **Moderate chemical** recipes contain small amounts of these natural chemicals and should suit all but the most sensitive individuals.

allergens All the recipes indicate if they include dairy, egg, nuts, gluten (wheat) and soy. Where possible, we've specified an alternative to eggs and dairy. Carob chips have been used as a chocolate substitute, but be aware that many are contaminated with dairy and may contain soy. Check the labels of all store bought ingredients carefully to ensure they don't contain allergen traces. The few recipes in the books that include nuts should be strictly avoided by those with an allergy to *any* kind of nut.

variations Many recipes give a variation. Read the variation carefully before you do your shopping so you buy the correct ingredients.

gluten The gluten-free recipes were developed using a store bought soy-free, gluten-free flour, except where specified otherwise. You can also make your own gluten-free alternative (see the text box below).

GLUTEN-FREE FLOUR

Nothing quite replaces gluten, so do not expect the substitute to be exactly the same. In baking, a mixture of flours works best, such as one part each of rice flour, potato flour and arrowroot, or one part each of rice flour, potato flour, arrowroot and maize cornstarch (cornflour). Sift the flours together three times before using, then substitute by weight, not by volume, when converting recipes. The addition of xanthan or guar gum (from health food stores) will also greatly improve the texture of your gluten-free flour. For cakes, add ¼ teaspoon gum per 1 cup (150 g) of gluten-free flour; for breads, add 1 teaspoon gum per cup of flour; for pizza crusts, add 2 teaspoons gum per cup of flour.

By now, everyone knows that breakfast is the most important meal of the day. Not only does it set you up for the day by providing energy for the hours ahead, it also stimulates your digestive system. Today, there is a wide range of good store bought cereals for people with food intolerances, but this chapter has some really interesting options, such as pancakes, muffins, crumpets and waffles for when cereal just isn't enough.

breakfast

porridge

Low chemical.
Contains gluten. Free of egg, dairy, nut and soy.

4 cups (400 g) rolled oats
I cup (105 g) rice flakes
I cup (130 g) barley flakes
I cup (130 g) rye flakes
I cup (205 g) millet
pinch of salt
I liter (4 cups) water

Prep time: 10 minutes
Cooking time: 20 minutes
Makes 8 cups

Put the rolled oats, rice flakes, barley flakes, rye flakes and millet in a large bowl and stir together thoroughly. Store the dry porridge mixture in an airtight container until ready to use.

To prepare the porridge for four people, put 2 cups (280 g) of the dry porridge mixture, a pinch of salt and 2 cups (500 ml) water in a saucepan, then stir well. Leave for 5 minutes (this creates a smoother, creamier porridge). Stir the porridge a few times, then pour in another 2 cups (500 ml) water. Bring to a boil over medium heat, stirring occasionally. Reduce the heat to low and simmer, stirring frequently, for 12–15 minutes, or until the mixture is soft and creamy and the grains are cooked.

HINT: Serve the porridge with your choice of milk or a substitute, such as soy milk or rice milk, and a drizzle of golden syrup, pure maple syrup or sugar. We have served ours with natural yogurt and golden syrup.

Wheat, barley, oats and rye contain gluten. If you are intolerant to gluten, be sure to check the ingredients lists of any commercially prepared breakfast cereals. For a low chemical cereal, avoid any with corn, dried fruit, coconut, honey, nuts, flavors and colors.

rolled rice porridge

Low chemical.
Free of egg, dairy, gluten, nut and soy.

½ cup (50 g) rolled rice
or rice flakes

2 cups (500 ml) boiling water

golden syrup, to serve

peeled and chopped pear,
to serve

Pear Juice (see Basics),
to serve

Prep time: 5 minutes
Cooking time: 20 minutes
Serves 4

Combine the rolled rice and water in a saucepan. Cover with a lid and simmer over medium heat for 20 minutes, or until soft and creamy. Serve topped with golden syrup, chopped pear and pear juice.

HINT: If you'd like a sweeter porridge, try adding a little pear juice in place of the water. You'll need to bring it to a boil before using it.

creamy rice porridge

Low chemical.
Free of egg, dairy, gluten, nut and soy.

For a deliciously creamy taste, make the porridge with a non-dairy alternative, such as rice milk. Bring 2 cups (500 ml) rice milk to a boil in a saucepan, then proceed with the recipe.

wheat-free muesli

Low chemical.
Free of egg, dairy, gluten, nut and soy.

2 cups (210 g) rice flakes
I cup (90 g) rice bran
peeled and chopped pear,
to serve
Pear Juice (see Basics), to serve

Prep time: 5 minutes
Cooking time: Nil
Makes 3 cups

Put the rice flakes and rice bran in a bowl and stir together thoroughly. Store in an airtight container until ready to use.

When ready to serve, top with chopped pear and pear juice.

HINT: For a softer textured muesli, soak the required amount of dry mix overnight, using just enough pear juice to moisten.

toasted wheat-free muesli

Low chemical.
Free of egg, dairy, gluten, nut and soy.

2 cups (210 g) rice flakes
I cup (90 g) rice bran
2 tablespoons canola oil
2 tablespoons golden syrup
peeled and chopped pear,
to serve
Pear Juice (see Basics),
to serve

Prep time: 5 minutes
Cooking time: 5 minutes
Makes 3 cups

Preheat the oven to 350°F (180°C/Gas 4). Combine the rice flakes and rice bran in a bowl. Mix together the oil and golden syrup, then pour over the flakes and stir until well combined.

Spread the mixture onto a baking tray and bake for about 5 minutes, or until golden. Cool before storing in an airtight container.

When ready to serve, top with chopped pear and pear juice.

HINT: You can vary the amount of golden syrup to taste.

pancakes with ricotta filling

Low chemical.
Contains egg, dairy and gluten. Free of nut and soy.

1 cup (150 g) all-purpose (plain) flour

2 teaspoons baking powder

1 egg

1 tablespoon canola oil

1¼–1½ cups (310–375 ml) milk

extra canola oil, for greasing

pure confectioners' (icing) sugar, for dusting

RICOTTA FILLING

7 oz (200 g) ricotta cheese or cottage cheese, pushed through a sieve

1½ tablespoons pure maple syrup or golden syrup

Prep time: 10 minutes

Cooking time: 20 minutes

Makes 10 pancakes

Sift the flour and baking powder into a bowl and make a well in the center. Mix together the egg, oil and 1¼ cups (310 ml) of the milk, then add to the dry ingredients. Stir well until the batter is smooth and reaches the consistency of thin cream, adding the rest of the milk as necessary. Strain the batter into a vessel with a pouring lip.

Lightly brush an 8 in (20 cm) frying pan with oil and heat over medium heat. Pour in just enough batter to thinly cover the bottom of the pan. When the top of the pancake begins to set, use a spatula to turn it over. After browning the second side, transfer to a plate. Repeat with the remaining batter, greasing the pan between batches.

For the filling, put the ricotta cheese and maple syrup into a small bowl and mix together with a spoon.

Use about a tablespoon of filling in the center of each pancake. Roll up or fold into quarters and serve dusted with confectioners' sugar.

HINT: If you'd prefer, you can serve these pancakes with peeled and sliced pears and maple syrup or just with a drizzle of golden syrup. We've served ours with maple syrup.

gluten-free pancakes

Low chemical.
Free of egg, dairy, gluten, nut and soy.

1¼ cups (190 g) soy-free, gluten-free all-purpose (plain) flour

2 teaspoons gluten-free baking powder

1 egg, or equivalent egg substitute

1 tablespoon canola oil

1¼–1½ cups (310–375 ml) water

extra canola oil, for greasing

peeled and sliced pear, to serve

pure maple syrup or golden syrup, to serve

Prep time: 10 minutes
Cooking time: 20 minutes
Makes 10 pancakes

Sift the flour and baking powder into a bowl and make a well in the center. Mix together the egg, oil and 1¼ cups (310 ml) water, then add to the dry ingredients. Stir well until the batter is smooth and reaches the consistency of thin cream, adding the rest of the water as necessary. Strain the batter into a vessel with a pouring lip.

Lightly brush an 8 in (20 cm) frying pan with oil and heat over medium heat. Pour in just enough mixture to thinly cover the bottom of the pan. When the top of the pancake starts to set, use a spatula to turn it over. After browning the second side, transfer to a plate. Repeat with the remaining pancake batter, greasing the pan between batches.

Make the rest of the pancakes in the same way, placing one on top of the other. Serve with sliced pear and maple or golden syrup.

HINT: The pancake batter can be made the day before and stored in a covered container in the refrigerator.

Pure maple syrup, which is low in chemicals, is concentrated from the sap of the maple tree. Do not confuse it with the cheaper maple-flavored syrup, which is artificially colored and flavored.

buckwheat pancakes

Low chemical.
Free of egg, dairy, gluten, nut and soy.

1 cup (130 g) buckwheat flour

1 egg, or equivalent egg substitute

¾ cup (185 ml) water

canola oil, for greasing

½ cup (125 ml) pure maple syrup

Prep time: 10 minutes
Cooking time: 20 minutes
Makes 16–20 pancakes

Sift the flour into a bowl and make a well in the center. Add the combined egg and water. Beat with a wooden spoon until well combined and smooth. Pour the batter into a vessel with a pouring lip.

Brush an 8 in (20 cm) frying pan with oil and heat over medium heat. Pour in just enough batter to thinly cover the bottom of the pan. When the top of the pancake starts to set, turn it over with a spatula. After browning the second side, transfer to a plate. Repeat with the remaining pancake batter, greasing the pan between batches. Serve with a drizzle of maple syrup.

pear and chive muffins

Low chemical.
Free of egg, dairy, gluten, nut and soy.

canola oil, for greasing

2 cups (300 g) soy-free,
gluten-free self-raising flour

2 teaspoons gluten-free
baking powder

2 tablespoons soft
brown sugar

½ cup (100 g) drained,
chopped, canned pear

2 tablespoons finely chopped
fresh chives

1 cup (250 ml) rice milk

⅓ cup (80 ml) canola oil

2 eggs, or equivalent
egg substitute

Prep time: 15 minutes
Cooking time: 20 minutes
Makes 10 muffins

Preheat the oven to 350°F (180°C/Gas 4). Lightly grease ten ⅓ cup (80 ml) muffin holes with canola oil.

Sift the flour and baking powder into a large bowl. Add the sugar. Stir in the pear and chives. In a separate bowl, combine the rice milk, oil and egg. Add the milk mixture to the flour mixture. Use a large metal spoon to mix until just combined. Divide the batter evenly among the prepared muffin holes.

Bake for 18–20 minutes, or until a skewer inserted in the center comes out clean. Set aside in the tray for 5 minutes before turning out onto a wire rack to cool.

HINT: These muffins need to be eaten on the day they are made.

wheat flour muffins

Low chemical.
Free of egg, dairy, gluten, nut and soy.

Replace the gluten-free flour with 2 cups (300 g) self-raising flour and omit the baking powder. Cow's milk or soy milk can replace the rice milk, if they are suitable for your diet.

corn and chive muffins

Moderate chemical.
Free of egg, dairy, gluten, nut and soy.

For those who are not so sensitive, you can replace the pear with ½ cup (100 g) drained, canned corn kernels.

potato muffins

Low chemical.
Free of egg, dairy, gluten, nut and soy.

7 oz (200 g) white-skinned potatoes, peeled and roughly chopped

4½ oz (125 g) dairy-free margarine

½ cup (95 g) soft brown sugar

½ cup (90 g) rice flour

½ cup (75 g) potato flour

½ cup (50 g) arrowroot

½ cup (60 g) maize cornstarch (cornflour)

2 teaspoons gluten-free baking powder

½ cup (125 ml) Pear Juice (see Basics)

Prep time: 20 minutes
Cooking time: 30 minutes
Makes 18 muffins

Boil or steam the potatoes for 15 minutes, or until tender. Drain well, then return the potatoes to the pan and mash until smooth. You will need ½ cup (115 g) of mashed potato for this recipe.

Preheat the oven to 415°F (210°C/Gas 6–7). Lightly grease two ⅓ cup (80 ml) muffin tins. Beat the margarine and sugar together until light and fluffy. Add the cooled mashed potato, then stir in the sifted dry ingredients alternately with the pear juice.

Place teaspoons of the mixture into each muffin hole—you should fill around 18 holes. Bake for 10–12 minutes. Leave in the trays for 5 minutes before turning out onto a wire rack to cool.

HINT: We used small muffin tins. If large ones are used, fill each muffin hole two-thirds full. The recipe will make 12 large muffins.

butternut muffins

Moderate chemical.
Free of egg, dairy, gluten, nut and soy.

For the less sensitive, replace half the potato with butternut squash (pumpkin). Boil or steam 2¼ oz (60 g) peeled squash for 10 minutes, or until tender. Drain well. Mash with a potato masher. Beat with a wooden spoon to ensure there are no lumps. Follow the method above.

gluten-free crumpets

Low chemical.
Free of egg, dairy, gluten, nut and soy.

3 cups (450 g) soy-free, gluten-free self-raising flour

1 tablespoon superfine (caster) sugar

1 teaspoon ground sea salt

2 teaspoons (7 g package) dried yeast

1¾ cups (435 ml) lukewarm rice milk

80 ml (⅓ cup) lukewarm water

½ teaspoon baking soda (bicarbonate of soda)

canola oil, for greasing

dairy-free margarine, to serve

Pear Jam (see Basics), to serve

Prep time: 15 minutes + 1¼ hours rising
Cooking time: 45 minutes
Makes 10 crumpets

Combine the flour, sugar, salt and yeast in a large bowl. Pour in the rice milk and whisk well to combine. Cover and set aside in a warm place for 1 hour, or until doubled in size.

Use a spoon to beat the mixture until it deflates. Combine the water and baking soda in a small bowl, then whisk into the batter until smooth. Set aside for 15 minutes.

Brush a large heavy-based non-stick frying pan with oil and heat over medium heat. Brush four 3¾ x ¾ in (9.5 x 2 cm) crumpet rings with oil, then place in the pan and reduce the heat to low.

Pour enough batter into each crumpet ring to fill three-quarters full. Cook for 12–15 minutes, or until large bubbles come to the surface, the base is golden and the top is set (if the bubbles don't pop you can use a thin wooden skewer to pierce the holes). Cover the pan and cook for a further 2–3 minutes. Use a sharp knife to carefully loosen the crumpets and remove from the rings. Put the crumpets on a wire rack. Wash the crumpet rings and re-grease. Repeat with the remaining batter. Serve with dairy-free margarine and pear jam.

Rice milk is high in carbohydrates and low in protein and Vitamin A, so it is not suitable for infants and young children as a milk substitute.

crumpets

Low chemical.
Contains dairy and gluten. Free of egg, nut and soy.

3 cups (450 g) all-purpose (plain) flour

1 tablespoon superfine (caster) sugar

1 teaspoon ground sea salt

2 teaspoons (7 g package) dried yeast

2¼ cups (560 ml) milk

1 cup (250 ml) lukewarm water

½ teaspoon baking soda (bicarbonate of soda)

canola oil, for greasing

butter, to serve

Pear Jam (see Basics), to serve

Prep time: 15 minutes + 1¼ hours rising

Cooking time: 45 minutes

Makes 12 crumpets

Combine the flour, sugar, salt and yeast in a large bowl. Pour in the milk and whisk well to combine. Cover and set aside in a warm place for 1 hour, or until doubled in size.

Use a spoon to beat the mixture until it deflates. Combine the water and baking soda, then whisk into the batter until smooth. Set aside for 15 minutes.

Brush a large heavy-based non-stick frying pan with oil and heat over medium heat. Brush four 3¾ x ¾ in (9.5 x 2 cm) crumpet rings with oil, then place in the pan and reduce the heat to low.

Pour enough batter into each crumpet ring to fill two-thirds full. Cook for 12–15 minutes, or until large bubbles come to the surface, the base is golden and the top is set (if the bubbles don't pop, you can use a thin wooden skewer to pierce the holes). Cover the pan and cook for a further 2–3 minutes. Use a sharp knife to carefully loosen the crumpets and remove from the rings. Place the crumpets on a wire rack. Wash the crumpet rings and re-grease. Repeat with the remaining batter. Serve with butter and pear jam.

The intake of Vitamin A and folic acid may be low on a restricted diet. Choose a supplement that provides the recommended daily intake and contains no flavors, additives, gluten or PABA.

gluten-free waffles

Low chemical.
Contains soy. Free of egg, dairy, gluten and nut.

2 cups (250 g) soy-containing, gluten-free self-raising flour

¼ cup (55 g) superfine (caster) sugar

10½ fl oz (300 ml) rice milk

2 eggs, or equivalent egg substitute

2¼ oz (60 g) dairy-free margarine, melted, cooled

Prep time: 10 minutes + 15 minutes resting

Cooking time: 30 minutes

Makes 6 waffles

Sift the flour into a large bowl. Stir in the sugar. In a separate bowl, whisk the rice milk and egg together. Pour the rice milk mixture into the flour and whisk until smooth. Whisk in the melted margarine. Set the batter aside to rest for 10–15 minutes.

Preheat a waffle maker. Pour ⅓-cupfuls (80 ml) of the batter into the waffle maker and cook following the waffle maker's instructions. Transfer to a wire rack and repeat with the remaining batter, allowing the waffle maker to reheat between waffles.

gluten-free sweet carob waffles

Low chemical.
Contains soy. Free of egg, dairy, gluten and nut.

Increase the rice milk to 1⅓ cups (330 ml) and heat until warm. Whisk the warm drink and ¼ cup (30 g) carob powder until smooth. Set aside to cool. Continue with the basic recipe, using the carob rice milk in place of the plain rice milk.

gluten-free savory corn and scallion waffles

Moderate chemical.
Contains soy. Free of egg, dairy, gluten and nut.

Reduce the superfine (caster) sugar to 2 tablespoons. Add ½ cup (100 g) drained, canned corn kernels and ¼ cup (30 g) finely chopped scallions (spring onions) or 1 bunch (15 g) finely chopped chives with the sugar, then continue with the recipe. Pour ½-cupfuls (125 ml) of the batter into the waffle maker. Makes 5–6 waffles.

plain waffles

Low chemical.
Contains egg, dairy and gluten. Free of nut and soy.

1¾ cups (265 g) all-purpose (plain) flour

1½ teaspoons baking powder

¼ cup (55 g) superfine (caster) sugar

1⅓ cups (330 ml) milk

2 eggs

2¼ oz (60 g) butter, melted, cooled

Prep time: 10 minutes + 15 minutes resting
Cooking time: 30 minutes
Makes 6 waffles

Sift the flour and baking powder into a large bowl. Stir in the sugar. In a separate bowl, whisk the milk and eggs together. Pour the milk mixture into the flour with the butter and whisk until smooth. Set the batter aside to rest for 10–15 minutes.

Preheat a waffle maker. Pour ⅓-cupfuls (80 ml) of the mixture into the waffle maker and cook following the waffle maker's instructions. Transfer to a wire rack and repeat with the remaining batter, allowing the waffle maker to reheat between waffles.

When choosing a non-dairy milk substitute, always choose a calcium-fortified replacement, such as soy milk or rice milk. Otherwise, you will need to take a calcium supplement that provides 600 mg per day.

carob waffles

Low chemical.
Contains egg, dairy and gluten. Free of nut and soy.

Reduce the flour to 1½ cups (225 g) all-purpose (plain) flour. Add ¼ cup (30 g) carob powder with the flour when sifting, then continue with the basic recipe.

baked eggs in potato

Low chemical.
Contains egg. Free of dairy, gluten, nut and soy.

1 lb 5 oz (600 g) white-skinned potatoes, peeled and roughly chopped

canola oil, for greasing

½ cup (35 g) rice crumbs, approximately

1½ tablespoons dairy-free margarine

3 scallions (spring onions), finely chopped

ground sea salt

8 eggs

Prep time: 20 minutes
Cooking time: 30 minutes
Makes 8 baked eggs

Boil or steam the potatoes for 15 minutes, or until tender. Drain well, then return the potatoes to the pan and mash until smooth. You will need 2 cups (460 g) of plain mashed potato for this recipe.

Preheat the oven to 350°F (180°C/Gas 4). Lightly grease eight ⅓ cup (80 ml) muffin holes and coat lightly with the rice crumbs.

Melt the margarine in a small frying pan, add the scallions and cook, stirring, until soft. Combine the scallion mixture with the potato and add salt to taste. Divide the potato mixture evenly among the muffin holes and press gently over the base and up the sides.

Break an egg into each potato nest and bake for 10–15 minutes, or until the egg is just set. Allow to cool slightly and invert to remove from the muffin tin. Place egg-side up on serving plates.

HINT: To ensure you get a centered yolk, first break your eggs (one at a time) into a cup, then pour into the potato shell.

Peel potatoes thickly, as there are more natural chemicals near the surface. Never use potatoes with green skin.

potato and leek fritters

Low chemical.
Free of egg, dairy, gluten, nut and soy.

2 lb 12 oz (1.2 kg) white-skinned potatoes

1 leek, washed

2 eggs, lightly beaten, or equivalent egg substitute

1 tablespoon rice flour

ground sea salt

2 tablespoons canola oil

Prep time: 15 minutes
Cooking time: 20 minutes
Serves 4–6

Peel and grate the potatoes. Pat the potato dry and put in a bowl. Finely chop the leek and add it to the bowl with the potato. Add the eggs, rice flour and a pinch of salt. Mix until just combined.

Heat the oil in a large frying pan. Drop tablespoons of the mixture into the pan—you may need to do this in batches. Fry on each side for a few minutes, or until golden brown. Serve hot or cold either on their own or with baked beans (see the recipe on the facing page).

HINT: Peeled potato will discolor if left to stand too long.

Use plain brushed potatoes. Red-skinned and new potatoes have moderate levels of natural flavor substances.

baked beans

Low chemical.
Free of egg, dairy, gluten, nut and soy.

1½ cups (300 g) dried beans, flageolet or cannellini

1 leek, washed and sliced

2 sprigs parsley

1 garlic clove, peeled

2 x 2 in (5 cm) pieces celery

2 tablespoons soft brown sugar

¼ teaspoon citric acid

¾ teaspoon saffron threads

sea salt

Prep time: 15 minutes + overnight soaking
Cooking time: 1¼ hours
Serves 4–6

Wash the beans and place in a large bowl. Cover with 1.5 liters (6 cups) water and soak overnight. Drain.

Place the beans and leek in a saucepan. Tie the parsley, garlic and celery—this is called a bouquet garni—together firmly with string and add to the saucepan. Pour in enough water to cover the beans. Simmer, uncovered for about 1 hour, or until tender. Remove the bouquet garni with tongs.

Add the sugar, citric acid, saffron and salt to taste. Simmer for 10 minutes longer. Serve hot, either with potato and leek fritters (see the recipe on the facing page) or on their own.

HINT: Citric acid is used in these recipes, as it is more likely to be tolerated than lemon juice or vinegar.

Whether you're looking for a light lunch, a simple supper, something savory to nibble with a drink, or a healthy after-school snack, you'll find plenty that's tempting here. Quick, nourishing, and with loads of variety, all the recipes in this chapter have been chosen to fit within the low chemical guidelines, so you can safely enjoy a delicious snack at any time without worrying about the consequences.

light bites

mini leek quiches

Low chemical.
Contains dairy. Free of egg, gluten, nut and soy.

canola oil, for greasing

1 lb 5 oz (600 g) white-skinned potatoes, peeled and chopped

2 tablespoons canola oil

2 cups (300 g) soy-free, gluten-free self-raising flour

1 teaspoon gluten-free baking powder

1 teaspoon ground sea salt

2 eggs, or equivalent egg substitute

LEEK FILLING

1½ oz (40 g) butter

1 leek, washed and thinly sliced

ground sea salt

3 eggs, or equivalent egg substitute

¾ cup (185 ml) milk

¾ cup (180 g) sour cream

Prep time: 20 minutes
Cooking time: 50 minutes
Makes 24 mini quiches

Preheat the oven to 350°F (180°C/Gas 4). Lightly grease two 12-cup cupcake tins. Boil or steam the potatoes for 15 minutes, or until tender. Drain well, then mash until smooth. You will need 2 cups (460 g) warm mashed potato for this recipe.

Combine the mashed potato and oil in a large bowl. Add the sifted dry ingredients, salt and enough egg to mix to a smooth dough. Knead on a lightly floured board until smooth. Roll out the pastry until ¼ in (5 mm) thick. Cut into 2½–2¾ in (6–7 cm) rounds and place in the prepared tins. Bake for 5 minutes, then press out any air bubbles in the pastry. Cool. Increase the oven to 400°F (200°C/Gas 6).

For the filling, melt the butter in a heavy-based saucepan over medium heat. Add the leek and cook, stirring often, for 5–6 minutes until tender. Allow to cool. Season with salt.

Whisk the eggs, milk and sour cream together in a bowl until well combined. Divide the leek mixture evenly among the pastry cases, then pour the egg mixture over the filling. Bake for 15–20 minutes, or until set and golden brown. Serve hot or cold.

HINT: The quiches can be made the day before and refrigerated in an airtight container. Reheat for 10 minutes in a 300°F (150°C/Gas 2) oven.

quiche pastry with wheat flour

Low chemical.
Contains gluten. Free of egg, dairy, nut and soy.

If you are not gluten-intolerant, you can simply use 2 cups (300 g) self-raising flour in the recipe above and omit the baking powder.

mini sweet potato quiches

Moderate chemical.
Contains dairy. Free of egg, gluten, nut and soy.

canola oil, for greasing

3 cups (450 g) soy-free, gluten-free all-purpose (plain) flour

7 oz (200 g) butter

2 eggs, lightly beaten, or equivalent egg substitute

2 tablespoons water, approximately

SWEET POTATO FILLING

14 oz (400 g) sweet potato, peeled and cut into ½ in (1 cm) dice

canola oil spray

ground sea salt

7 oz (200 g) ricotta cheese, crumbled

2 tablespoons finely chopped fresh chives

3 eggs, or equivalent egg substitute

¾ cup (185 ml) milk

¾ cup (180 g) sour cream

Prep time: 25 minutes
Cooking time: 35 minutes
Makes 24 mini quiches

Preheat the oven to 400°F (200°C/Gas 6). Lightly grease a baking tray and two 12-cup cupcake tins.

Sift the flour into a large bowl. Rub in the butter with your fingertips until the mixture resembles dry breadcrumbs. Make a well in the center and add the lightly beaten eggs and the water, or enough to form a soft dough. Turn out onto a lightly floured board and knead lightly. Roll out between two sheets of lightly floured baking paper to about ⅛ in (3 mm) thick. Cut into 2½–2¾ in (6–7 cm) rounds and place in the prepared tins.

For the sweet potato filling, put the sweet potato on the prepared tray. Spray with oil and season with a little salt. Bake for 15 minutes, or until golden brown. Cool. Combine the sweet potato with the crumbled ricotta cheese and chopped chives.

Combine the eggs, milk and sour cream in a bowl until well combined. Divide the vegetable mixture evenly among the pastry cases, then pour the egg mixture over the filling. Bake for 15–20 minutes, or until golden brown. Serve hot or cold.

HINT: The quiches can be made the day before and refrigerated in an airtight container. Reheat for 10 minutes in a 300°F (150°C/Gas 2) oven.

chickpea dip

Low chemical.
Free of egg, dairy, gluten, nut and soy.

4½ oz (125 g) canned chickpeas, rinsed and drained

¼ teaspoon citric acid

¼ cup (60 ml) Pear Juice (see Basics)

2 garlic cloves, crushed

2 tablespoons canola oil

2 tablespoons water

ground sea salt

Prep time: 15 minutes
Cooking time: Nil
Makes 1 cup

Combine the chickpeas, citric acid, pear juice, garlic, oil and water in a food processor. Blend or process until smooth—the mixture should be the consistency of thick mayonnaise. Season with salt to taste.

Scoop into a bowl and serve with crispy wafer crackers (see the recipe on page 56) or chilled sticks of allowed vegetables, such as celery.

HINT: If canned chickpeas are unavailable, soak ¼ cup (50 g) dried chickpeas in cold water overnight, then drain. Place in a saucepan with water and bring to a boil. Reduce the heat and simmer for about 2½ hours, or until tender. Drain well and proceed with the recipe.

chickpea and cashew dip

Low chemical.
Contains nuts. Free of egg, dairy, gluten and soy.

For a delicious nutty flavor to this dip, process ¾ cup (115 g) cashews to a smooth paste in a small food processor and add it to the chickpea mixture. Makes 1½ cups.

spring rolls

Low chemical.
Contains gluten. Free of egg, dairy, nut and soy.

FILLING
1 tablespoon canola oil

1 garlic clove, crushed

3 scallions (spring onions), finely chopped

4½ oz (125 g) ground (minced) veal

½ cup (40 g) shredded cabbage

¼ cup (20 g) mung beans

¼ cup (40 g) shredded bamboo shoots

ground sea salt

24 spring roll wrappers

1 tablespoon maize cornstarch (cornflour), blended with 2 tablespoons water

canola oil, for deep-frying

DIPPING SAUCE
⅓ cup (80 ml) water

1 teaspoon canola oil

1 garlic clove, crushed

1 teaspoon citric acid

1½ tablespoons soft brown sugar

Prep time: 35 minutes

Cooking time: 20 minutes

Makes 24 rolls

For the filling, heat the oil in a frying pan, add the garlic, scallions and veal and cook over medium heat for 5–6 minutes, or until browned. Add the cabbage, mung beans and bamboo shoots, then season with salt. Cook for a further 2–3 minutes, or until softened. Allow to cool.

Put 1 heaping teaspoon of mixture on the lower corner of each spring roll wrapper. Brush all the edges with the cornstarch mixture. Fold the lower corner over the filling and roll up, tucking in the ends as you roll. Press to seal. Repeat with the rest of the wrappers and filling.

Fill a large saucepan or deep-fat fryer one-third full of oil and heat to 350°F (180°C), or until a cube of bread dropped into the oil browns in 15 seconds. Deep-fry the spring rolls in batches until crisp and golden. Drain on paper towels. Serve immediately with the dipping sauce.

To make the dipping sauce, combine all the ingredients in a small bowl.

fresh spring rolls

Low chemical.
Free of egg, dairy, gluten, nut and soy.

Adjust the filling: double the amount of veal, cabbage and sprouts, add 1 extra scallion (spring onion) and omit the bamboo shoots. Cook and cool the filling as described above. Thinly slice 1 carrot and cut 3 oz (85 g) celery into thin strips. Wash 8 butter lettuce leaves. Brush a large round rice paper wrapper with water on both sides. Set aside for 1–2 minutes to soften. Put a lettuce leaf in the center of the wrapper. Top with one-eighth each of the filling, carrot and celery. Fold up the bottom of the wrapper, then fold in the sides and roll up to enclose. Cover with a damp tea towel. Repeat with seven more wrappers and the remaining ingredients. Serve with the dipping sauce. Makes 8.

crispy wafer crackers

Low chemical.
Free of egg, dairy, gluten, nut and soy.

canola oil, for greasing
1 cup (180 g) rice flour
1 cup (120 g) maize cornstarch (cornflour)
½ cup (45 g) rice bran
½ teaspoon ground sea salt
¾ cup (185 ml) water
2 tablespoons canola oil

Prep time: 10 minutes
Cooking time: 25 minutes
Makes about 40 crackers

Preheat the oven to 400°F (200°C/Gas 6). Lightly oil two 12 × 10 in (30 × 25 cm) jelly-roll tins.

Combine the dry ingredients in a bowl, make a well in the middle and add combined water and oil. Mix until well combined.

Divide the mixture into two portions. Press each portion of dough into a prepared tin and bake for 20–25 minutes. Cool in the tin. Break into pieces and store in an airtight container for up to 2 days.

HINT: If you'd like more evenly shaped crackers, score the dough in the tins with a knife before you bake them, then the crackers will be easy to break neatly once they're cooked.

crispy poppy seed wafer crackers

Low chemical.
Free of egg, dairy, gluten, nut and soy.

Lightly brush the dough with 1 lightly beaten egg, or equivalent egg substitute, and sprinkle with 2 tablespoons poppy seeds before baking.

crispy potato bites

Low chemical.
Free of egg, dairy, gluten, nut and soy.

11½ oz (325 g) white-skinned potatoes, peeled and roughly chopped

2 tablespoons canola oil

3 finely chopped scallions (spring onions)

½ cup (60 g) maize cornstarch (cornflour)

¼ cup (40 g) potato flour

1 teaspoon gluten-free baking powder

½ teaspoon ground sea salt

1 tablespoon finely chopped fresh chives

1 egg, or equivalent egg substitute

1–2 tablespoons water

canola oil, for deep-frying

ground sea salt, extra

Prep time: 35 minutes
Cooking time: 30 minutes
Makes about 60

Boil or steam the potatoes for 15 minutes, or until tender. Drain well, then return the potatoes to the pan and mash until smooth. You will need 1 cup (230 g) warm mashed potato for this recipe.

Transfer the warm mashed potato to a bowl. Add the oil and scallions and stir until combined. Add the sifted dry ingredients, salt, chives and egg. Mix and knead using your hands, adding the water until the mixture is well combined and forms a smooth ball.

Knead the dough gently on a board lightly dusted with cornstarch. Break off pieces of dough and roll into hazelnut-sized balls.

Fill a large saucepan or deep-fat fryer one-third full of oil and heat to 350°F (180°C), or until a cube of bread dropped into the oil browns in 15 seconds. Deep-fry the potato balls in batches for 2–3 minutes, or until they puff slightly and turn golden brown. Remove from the oil using a slotted spoon, then drain on paper towel. Serve immediately, sprinkled with extra salt if desired.

HINT: The mixture can be made the day before and stored in a sealed plastic bag in the refrigerator. Knead the dough to soften before rolling it.

Store-bought potato products, such as potato chips (crisps), may contain preservatives (220, 228), or antioxidants, if cooked in oil.

crispy corn and potato bites

Moderate chemical.
Free of egg, dairy, gluten, nut and soy.

For the less sensitive, add ½ cup (100 g) drained, canned corn kernels with the scallions and proceed with the recipe.

chicken and leek puffs

Low chemical.
Free of egg, dairy, gluten, nut and soy.

1 cup (250 ml) water

⅓ cup (80 ml) canola oil

¾ cup (115 g) soy-free, gluten-free all-purpose (plain) flour

¼ teaspoon baking soda (bicarbonate of soda)

¾ teaspoon gluten-free baking powder

3 eggs, or equivalent egg substitute

CHICKEN AND LEEK FILLING

2 tablespoons dairy-free margarine

5½ oz (150 g) chicken breast fillet

½ leek, washed and thinly sliced

1 tablespoon soy-free, gluten-free all-purpose (plain) flour

¼ cup (60 ml) rice milk

¼ cup (60 ml) Chicken Stock (see Basics)

ground sea salt

1 tablespoon chopped parsley

Prep time: 1 hour
Cooking time: 40 minutes
Makes 24 puffs

Preheat the oven to 415°F (210°C/Gas 6–7). Cover two baking trays with baking paper. Pour the water and oil into a saucepan and bring to a boil. Remove from the heat, add the sifted dry ingredients, then return to the heat and stir constantly until the mixture thickens and leaves the side of the saucepan (it may look a little oily). Scoop into the small bowl of an electric mixer and allow to cool slightly.

Beat the mixture, adding the eggs one at a time and beating well between each addition, until it is thick and shiny. Place level tablespoons of the mixture onto the prepared trays. Spray lightly all over with cold water, to aid rising. Bake for 10 minutes, or until they rise and start to brown. Reduce the heat to 375°F (190°C/Gas 5) and bake for 10–15 minutes, or until cooked through. Remove the puffs from the oven and allow to cool on a wire rack.

For the chicken and leek filling, melt 1 tablespoon of the margarine in a frying pan over medium heat, add the chicken breast and fry for 3 minutes on each side, or until cooked through. Remove from the pan and cut into small pieces. Melt the remaining margarine in a saucepan, add the leek and cook, stirring often, for 5–6 minutes, or until soft. Sprinkle over the flour and cook, stirring, for 20 seconds. Add the combined rice milk and stock, stirring over the heat until the mixture boils and thickens. Season with a little salt. Add the chicken and parsley to the white sauce and heat gently until warmed through.

Split the puffs in half, spoon in the warm filling, then replace the tops. Serve while warm.

HINT: The puffs can be made and stored unfilled in an airtight container for 1 week. If they become soft, they can be re-crisped in a 300°F (150°C/Gas 2) oven for 5–10 minutes.

egg and chive puffs

Low chemical.
Contains egg. Free of dairy, gluten, nut and soy.

24 puffs (see Chicken and
Leek Puffs, page 58)

**EGG AND
CHIVE FILLING**

2 tablespoons dairy-free
margarine

1 leek, washed and
thinly sliced

¼ teaspoon sugar

1 tablespoon soy-free,
gluten-free all-purpose
(plain) flour

¼ cup (60 ml) rice milk

¼ cup (60 ml) Chicken Stock
(see Basics)

ground sea salt

4 hard-boiled eggs,
finely chopped

1 tablespoon finely chopped
fresh chives

Prep time: 1 hour
Cooking time: 40 minutes
Makes 24 puffs

Melt 1 tablespoon of the margarine in a frying pan over medium heat, add the leek and sugar and cook, stirring often, for 5–6 minutes, or until the leek is softened. Remove from the pan and set aside.

Melt the remaining margarine in a saucepan over medium heat, add the flour and cook, stirring, for 20 seconds. Gradually add the combined rice milk and stock, stirring until the mixture boils and thickens. Season with salt to taste. Add the leek mixture to the white sauce with the hard-boiled eggs and chives and heat gently until warmed through. Season with salt to taste.

Split the puffs in half, spoon in the warm egg and chive filling, then replace the tops. Serve while warm.

asparagus and leek puffs

Moderate chemical.
Contains dairy. Free of egg, gluten, nut and soy.

If you can tolerate dairy, make the white sauce with cow's milk and butter instead of rice milk and margarine. Omit the hard-boiled eggs and add 6¼ oz (180 g) thinly sliced and blanched asparagus and 1 tablespoon chopped chives to the sauce with the leek mixture. Heat gently until warmed through and season with salt to taste.

butter puffs with lamb

Low chemical.
Contains egg, dairy and gluten. Free of nut and soy.

¾ cup (185 ml) water
2¼ oz (60 g) butter
¾ cup (115 g) all-purpose (plain) flour
3 eggs

LAMB FILLING
7 oz (200 g) cold cooked lamb, finely chopped
¼ cup (60 g) Mayonnaise (see Basics)
1 tablespoon finely chopped fresh chives

Prep time: 1 hour
Cooking time: 40 minutes
Makes 24 puffs

Preheat the oven to 415°F (210°C/Gas 6–7). Cover two baking trays with baking paper. Put the water and butter into a saucepan and bring to a boil. Remove from the heat, sift in the flour, then return to the heat and stir constantly until the mixture thickens and leaves the side of the saucepan (it may look a little oily). Transfer the mixture into the small bowl of an electric mixer and allow to cool slightly.

Beat the mixture, adding the eggs one at a time and beating well between each addition, until it is thick and shiny. Put level tablespoons of the mixture onto the prepared tray. Spray lightly all over with cold water, to aid rising. Bake for 10 minutes, or until they rise and start to brown. Reduce the heat to 375°F (190°C/Gas 5) and bake for a further 10–15 minutes, or until cooked through. Remove the puffs from the oven and allow to cool.

To make the lamb filling, combine the lamb, mayonnaise and chives. Spoon the cold mixture into the cooled, crisp puffs.

HINT: Depending on your particular intolerance and level of sensitivity, you can combine the filling that suits you with the puff that you prefer.

potato and egg puffs

Low chemical.
Contains egg. Free of dairy, gluten, nut and soy.

Heat 1 tablespoon canola oil in a frying pan. Add 1 large peeled and cubed white-skinned potato, cover and cook for 5–6 minutes, or until the potato is cooked. Add 3 beaten eggs and stir gently with a fork until the egg is cooked. Be careful not to break up the potato cubes. Spoon the warm filling into the puffs of your choice and serve.

vegetable strudels

Low chemical.
Free of egg, dairy, gluten, nut and soy.

1 heaping cup (165 g) potato flour

1½ cups (265 g) rice flour

3 teaspoons gluten-free baking powder

4½ oz (125 g) dairy-free margarine

⅓–½ cup (80–125 ml) water, plus extra, for glazing

canola oil, for deep-frying

VEGETABLE FILLING

2 teaspoons dairy-free margarine

2 tablespoons canola oil

1 garlic clove, crushed

10½ oz (300 g) white-skinned potatoes, peeled, chopped and partly cooked

1 cup (150 g) rutabaga (swede), cubed and partly cooked

½ cup (60 g) chopped green beans

3 scallions (spring onions), thinly sliced

Prep time: 50 minutes

Cooking time: 25 minutes

Makes 16 strudels

Sift the dry ingredients into a bowl. Rub the margarine in with your fingertips until the mixture resembles fine breadcrumbs. Make a well in the center. Add enough water to make a soft dough. Turn onto a rice-floured board and knead lightly. Divide the dough into four equal portions. Roll each portion out into a 12½ in (32 cm) square, ¼ in (5 mm) thick, between two sheets of baking paper. Cut each square into four squares—you should have 16 squares in all.

For the vegetable filling, put the margarine and oil into a saucepan. Heat over medium heat until the margarine melts. Add the garlic, vegetables and scallions and mix well. Cook, covered, over low heat for 6 minutes, or until the vegetables are tender. Set aside to cool completely (if the filling is warm it will soften and split the dough).

Divide the filling evenly among the dough squares. Brush the edges with water and fold the corners over to envelop the filling.

Fill a large saucepan or deep-fat fryer one-third full with oil and heat to 350°F (180°C), or until a cube of bread dropped into the oil browns in 15 seconds. Deep-fry the strudels in small batches. Drain on paper towels. Keep hot in a warm oven until all are cooked. Serve hot.

cheesy egg and vegetable strudels

Low chemical.
Contains egg and dairy. Free of gluten, nut and soy.

Make the dough using milk and butter instead of water and margarine. Reduce the rutabaga to 75 g (½ cup) and add 2 chopped hard-boiled eggs and ½ cup (125 g) cottage cheese to the cooled vegetable mixture.

cheese pinwheels

Low chemical.
Contains dairy. Free of egg, gluten, nut and soy.

canola oil, for greasing
¾ cup (115 g) potato flour
1 cup (180 g) rice flour
2 teaspoons gluten-free baking powder
3 oz (85 g) butter
¼–⅓ cup (60–80 ml) milk
milk or water, for glazing
1 tablespoon poppy seeds

RICOTTA FILLING
¾ cup (185 g) ricotta cheese
2 scallions (spring onions), finely chopped

Prep time: 20 minutes
Cooking time: 15 minutes
Serves 4–6

Preheat the oven to 350°F (180°C/Gas 4). Lightly grease a shallow 8 in (20 cm) round tin with canola oil.

Sift the dry ingredients into a bowl. Rub the butter in with your fingertips until the mixture resembles fine breadcrumbs. Make a well in the center. Add enough milk to make a soft dough. Turn out onto a rice-floured board and knead lightly.

Roll the dough into a ¼ in (5 mm) thick rectangle between two sheets of baking paper. Turn and release the paper frequently to prevent the dough from sticking to the paper.

For the ricotta filling, beat the ricotta cheese in a bowl until creamy. Add the scallions and mix well. Spread on the dough.

Use the baking paper to help you roll up the dough. Once you have a roll, cut it into ¾ in (2 cm) thick slices. Place the slices, cut side up, into the prepared tin. Glaze with milk or water and sprinkle the top with poppy seeds. Bake for 12–15 minutes. Serve hot or cold.

veal and chicken terrine

Low chemical.
Contains alcohol. Free of egg, dairy, gluten, nut and soy.

canola oil, for greasing

2 tablespoons canola oil

2 garlic cloves, crushed

1 leek, washed and finely chopped

2 lb 4 oz (1 kg) ground (minced) veal

3 tablespoons finely chopped fresh chives

3 eggs, lightly beaten, or equivalent egg substitute

2 tablespoons canola oil, extra

¼ cup (60 ml) gin

1½ teaspoons ground sea salt

½ cup (40 g) fresh gluten-free breadcrumbs

2 (12 oz/340 g) chicken breast fillets, each cut into four long strips

Prep time: 45 minutes
Cooking time: 1½ hours
Serves 6–8

Preheat the oven to 350°F (180°C/Gas 4). Grease a 4 x 8 in (10 x 20 cm) loaf tin, then line with aluminium foil.

Heat the oil in a frying pan over medium heat, add the garlic and leek and fry for 5–6 minutes, or until soft. Allow to cool. Transfer to a bowl, then add the veal, chives, eggs, extra oil, gin, salt and breadcrumbs. Using your hands, mix and knead the mixture until well combined.

Put half of the veal mixture into the prepared tin, pressing down well. Lay the chicken breasts over the meat. Press the remaining veal mixture over the chicken. Cover with greased aluminium foil. Place in a baking dish and add enough boiling water to come halfway up the sides of the loaf tin. Bake for 1¼–1½ hours.

When cooked, remove the loaf tin from the dish of water; drain off any liquid. Put a piece of cardboard on top of the terrine, then weigh it down with a heavy weight (for instance, cans of food). Refrigerate until cold. Serve cut into thin slices with salad or as a sandwich filling.

When flying or driving, anticipate your needs and prepare some healthy snacks to take along. You can't always rely on airlines to supply special meals.

vegetable pouches

Moderate chemical.
Contains dairy. Free of egg, gluten, nut and soy.

1 cup (130 g) buckwheat flour

1 egg, or equivalent egg substitute

1¼ cups (315 ml) water

canola oil, for greasing

VEGETABLE FILLING

1 tablespoon canola oil

2 garlic cloves, crushed

1 cup (75 g) shredded red cabbage

1 cup (140 g) finely chopped celery

1 cup (155 g) peas, cooked

4 scallions (spring onions), chopped

16–20 chives, softened in hot water

COTTAGE CHEESE DRESSING

1 cup (250 g) cottage cheese

3½ fl oz (100 ml) Pear Juice (see Basics)

1 teaspoon citric acid

Prep time: 45 minutes

Cooking time: 25 minutes

Makes 16–20 pouches

Sift the flour into a bowl and make a well in the center. Add the combined egg and water. Beat with a wooden spoon until well combined and smooth. Pour the batter into a vessel with a pouring lip.

Brush an 8 in (20 cm) frying pan with oil. Heat over medium heat and pour in just enough batter to make a thin layer over the bottom of the pan. When the top of the pancake starts to set, turn it over with a spatula. After browning the second side, transfer to a plate and keep warm. Repeat with the remaining batter.

For the vegetable filling, heat the oil in a frying pan over medium heat. Add the garlic and cook for 1 minute. Add the cabbage, celery, peas and scallions. Cook for 3–4 minutes, or until the celery is tender.

Spoon the vegetable filling into the center of each pancake. Bring up the edges of the pancake to form a pouch. Wrap a chive around the neck of each pouch. Tie in a knot to secure. Put the pouches on a plate.

For the cottage cheese dressing, combine the cottage cheese, pear juice and citric acid in a blender or food processor. Blend on high for 2–3 minutes until well combined.

Serve the vegetable pouches with the cottage cheese dressing drizzled over or on the side, for dipping.

lentil and potato pie

Low chemical.
Free of egg, dairy, gluten, nut and soy.

1 lb 5 oz (600 g) white-skinned potatoes, peeled and roughly chopped

1½ cups (375 g) dried red lentils

2 tablespoons finely chopped fresh chives

ground sea salt

Prep time: 10 minutes
Cooking time: 55 minutes
Serves 4–6

Preheat the oven to 350°F (180°C/Gas 4). Lightly oil a 9 in (23 cm) pie plate. Boil or steam the potatoes for 15 minutes, or until tender. Drain well, then return the potatoes to the pan and mash until smooth. You will need 2 cups (460 g) of warm mashed potato for this recipe.

Wash the lentils under cold running water, then drain. Cover with cold water and bring to a boil. Boil gently for 15 minutes, or until soft. Drain well. Transfer to a blender or small food processor and purée.

Combine the lentils, potato, chives and salt to taste. Scoop into the prepared pie plate and bake for 25 minutes, or until brown. Serve hot.

vegetable soup

Low chemical.
Free of egg, dairy, gluten, nut and soy.

1 cup (200 g) small dried white or red beans

1 tablespoon canola oil

1 leek, halved lengthways, washed and thickly sliced

2 garlic cloves, peeled and crushed

14 oz (400 g) rutabaga (swede), peeled and chopped

3 celery stalks, chopped

1.5 liters (6 cups) Vegetable Stock (see Basics)

7 oz (200 g) green beans, sliced

ground sea salt

gluten-free crusty bread, to serve

Prep time: 15 minutes + overnight soaking

Cooking time: 1 hour 20 minutes

Serves 4–6

Wash the beans and then soak them overnight in water. Drain well.

Heat the oil in a large saucepan over medium heat. Cook the leek and garlic, stirring occasionally, for 4–5 minutes, or until the leek softens. Add the rutabaga and celery and cook for 2–3 minutes.

Add the drained beans and stock to the pan and bring to a boil. Simmer, partially covered, for 50–60 minutes, or until the beans are tender. Add the green beans and cook for a further 5–10 minutes, or until the green beans are tender. Season with salt to taste. Serve with gluten-free bread.

Children tend to grow out of their allergies by the age of five or six, though sometimes a particular food such as fish or nuts may need to be avoided for life.

potato and butternut soup

Moderate chemical.
Free of egg, dairy, gluten, nut and soy.

1 tablespoon canola oil

1 leek, halved lengthways, washed and sliced

2 garlic cloves, peeled and crushed

1 lb 2 oz (500 g) white-skinned potatoes, peeled and chopped

1 lb 2 oz (500 g) butternut squash (pumpkin), peeled, deseeded and chopped

1.25 liters (5 cups) Vegetable Stock (see Basics)

finely chopped fresh chives, to serve

gluten-free bread, to serve

Prep time: 30 minutes
Cooking time: 40 minutes
Serves 4

Heat the oil in a large saucepan over medium heat. Add the leek and garlic and cook, stirring, for 2 minutes. Reduce the heat to low. Cover the pan with a lid and cook, stirring occasionally, for 7–8 minutes, or until the leek is very soft.

Add the potato, squash and stock to the pan. Bring to a boil. Reduce the heat and simmer, partially covered, for 20–25 minutes, or until the vegetables are very soft. Set the pan aside for 10 minutes to allow the mixture to cool slightly.

Purée the soup in a blender or food processor (in batches, if necessary) until smooth. Divide the soup among serving bowls and sprinkle with chives. Serve with gluten-free bread.

HINT: If you can tolerate dairy, add 2 teaspoons of sour cream to each bowl of soup before serving, if desired.

Salicylates and amines can build up in your system and may only begin to cause symptoms after several days. Very sensitive people may get symptoms from smells and fumes as well as from food chemicals.

egg roll

Low chemical.
Contains nuts and egg. Free of dairy, gluten and soy.

4 eggs
½ teaspoon sugar
½ teaspoon ground sea salt
canola oil, for greasing

FILLING
3 tablespoons red kidney beans, mashed
⅓ cup (30 g) mung bean sprouts
⅓ cup (50 g) chopped raw cashews
1 tablespoon finely chopped fresh chives

Prep time: 15 minutes
Cooking time: 10 minutes
Serves 4

Preheat a broiler (grill) to medium heat. Lightly whisk the eggs, sugar and salt together just enough to combine the yolk and white. Pour into a 12 x 10 in (30 x 25 cm) greased jelly-roll tin. Broil (grill) for 10 minutes, or until the egg is set. Set aside to cool for 2–3 minutes. Turn the egg out onto a sheet of baking paper.

For the filling, combine the kidney beans, mung bean sprouts, cashews and chives. Spread evenly over the egg.

Roll up the egg and filling from one of the longest sides of the rectangle. Cut into slices and serve warm or cold.

HINT: Instead of broiling (grilling), the egg may be cooked in the oven at 350°F (180°C/Gas 4) until set.

Once you remove processed and packaged foods from your diet, you also remove a great deal of added salt. So don't be afraid to season your food to taste with a little salt—but remember to use only plain sea, rock or regular salt, and avoid vegetable flavored salts.

fish and bean soup

Low chemical.
Free of egg, dairy, gluten, nut and soy.

2 tablespoons canola oil

I large leek, washed and thinly sliced

I lb 2 oz (500 g) white-skinned potatoes, peeled and chopped

2 garlic cloves, crushed

1.5 liters (6 cups) Chicken Stock (see Basics)

9 oz (250 g) green beans, cut into 1¼ in (3 cm) pieces

I lb 2 oz (500 g) firm white boneless fish, cut into small cubes

3 scallions (spring onions), diagonally thinly sliced

ground sea salt

Prep time: 15 minutes
Cooking time: 30 minutes
Serves 4

Heat the oil in a large saucepan over medium heat. Cook the leek, stirring often, for 5–6 minutes, or until it softens.

Add the potato and garlic and cook, stirring, for 2 minutes. Pour in the stock, increase the heat to high and bring to a boil. Reduce the heat and simmer, partially covered, for 10 minutes, or until the potatoes are almost tender when tested with the point of a knife.

Add the beans and fish and continue to cook for a further 5 minutes, or until the fish and beans are cooked. Stir in the scallions. Taste and season with salt, if necessary.

rice and cottage cheese pie

Low chemical.
Contains egg and dairy. Free of gluten, nut and soy.

canola oil, for greasing

½ cup (100 g) white long-grain rice

2 tablespoons finely chopped fresh chives

1 oz (30 g) butter, melted

⅓ cup (90 g) cottage cheese

2 eggs, lightly beaten

FILLING

60 g (2¼ oz) butter

5 scallions (spring onions), chopped

4 eggs

1 cup (250 g) cottage cheese

ground sea salt

Prep time: 40 minutes

Cooking time: 1 hour

Serves 4–6

Preheat the oven to 325°F (170°C/Gas 3). Lightly grease a 9 in (23 cm) flan tin or pie plate with canola oil.

Bring a large saucepan of water to a boil. Add the rice and cook for 12 minutes, or until very tender, stirring occasionally. Drain and cool. You will need 1½ cups of cold cooked rice for this recipe. Combine the cooled rice with the chives, butter, cottage cheese and eggs and press into the base and sides of prepared pan. Chill for 30 minutes.

Meanwhile, prepare the filling. Melt the butter in a small saucepan over low heat. Add the scallions and cook for 8–10 minutes, or until soft, but not brown. Remove from the heat. Cool.

Combine the eggs, cottage cheese and a pinch of salt in a bowl. Add the scallion mixture and mix well. Pour the filling into the prepared crust. Bake for 40–45 minutes, or until firm and golden brown. Serve the pie hot or cold.

HINT: The rice should be very well cooked and slightly mushy. This can be achieved by stirring it once or twice during cooking.

asparagus and cottage cheese pie

Moderate chemical.
Contains egg and dairy. Free of gluten, nut and soy.

Add 3 oz (85 g) of fresh asparagus pieces to the cottage cheese filling, before pouring it into the crust.

spring salad

Low chemical.
Free of egg, dairy, gluten, nut and soy.

2 cups (500 ml) Chicken Stock
(see Basics)

7 oz (200 g) single chicken
breast fillet

4½ oz (125 g) green beans,
trimmed

½ small (600 g) white cabbage,
shredded finely

4 scallions (spring onions),
finely chopped

4 celery stalks, sliced thinly

⅓ cup (80 ml) Salad Dressing
(see Basics)

Prep time: 25 minutes

Cooking time: 15 minutes

Serves 4

Bring the chicken stock to a boil in a saucepan. Remove from the heat, add the chicken to the stock, then cover and allow to cool in the liquid. Be careful not to allow the chicken to boil in the liquid or it will become tough and dry. After about 10 minutes, the chicken should be cooked (this time may vary by 1–2 minutes).

Meanwhile, put the beans in a saucepan of boiling water, bring back to a boil and simmer for 30–60 seconds, or until the beans are bright green. Drain and plunge the beans into iced water to refresh them. Drain and pat dry on paper towels. Chop the beans finely.

Remove the chicken from the cooled stock and chop finely. Combine the chicken, beans, cabbage, scallions and celery in a large bowl. Pour the dressing over the salad. Toss lightly.

HINT: If you don't have any chicken stock for poaching the chicken, peel, wash and chop a leek and bring it to a boil in 2 cups (500 ml) water before adding the chicken fillet.

spring salad with cashew nut dressing

Low chemical.
Contains nuts. Free of egg, dairy, gluten and soy.

If you can tolerate nuts, replace half the salad dressing with ⅓ cup (90 g) ready-made cashew paste before dressing the salad. Sprinkle the salad with ¼ cup (35 g) chopped cashews.

warm quail salad

Low chemical.
Free of egg, dairy, gluten, nut and soy.

6 (2 lb 12 oz/1.25 kg) quail
⅓ cup (80 ml) canola oil
1 teaspoon citric acid
1 teaspoon ground sea salt
1 iceberg lettuce, torn into pieces
2 tablespoons finely chopped fresh chives
½ cup (125 ml) Salad Dressing (see Basics)
½ cup (125 ml) Pear Juice (see Basics)

Prep time: 40 minutes + marinating time
Cooking time: 15 minutes
Serves 4–6

Wash the quail and pat dry. Split down the back using poultry shears or a large, sharp knife, then open out flat. Put in a large shallow non-metallic dish. Coat with the combined oil, citric acid and salt. Cover and marinate for 2–3 hours, turning once during marinating.

Place the quail under a hot broiler (grill) for 10–15 minutes, or until cooked and browned.

Combine the lettuce and chives. Place on a large flat serving dish. Arrange the hot quail on top. Pour over the combined salad dressing and pear juice. Serve immediately.

HINTS: Quail has a slightly gamy flavor. It is very tender and should be cooked quickly under a hot broiler (grill) or in a hot oven. Always add some fat or oil to quail when cooking to prevent it from drying out.

Quail is usually eaten with the fingers so supply a finger bowl.

asian-style salad

Low chemical.
Contains egg. Free of dairy, gluten, nut and soy.

4½ oz (125 g) dried rice vermicelli

2 eggs

¼ small (300 g) white cabbage, shredded

3½ oz (100 g) cold cooked chicken, sliced

3½ oz (100 g) cold cooked lamb, sliced

2 tablespoons finely chopped fresh chives

DRESSING

¼ cup (55 g) sugar

¼ cup (60 ml) water

½ teaspoon citric acid

½ teaspoon ground sea salt

Prep time: 25 minutes
Cooking time: 15 minutes
Serves 4–6

Put the dried rice vermicelli in a bowl, cover with boiling water and soak for 6 minutes, or until softened. Drain, then run under cold water to cool the noodles. Drain thoroughly.

For the dressing, combine the sugar and water in a small saucepan. Stir over low heat until the sugar dissolves. Cook for 3–4 minutes, add the citric acid and salt, then remove the pan from the heat and cool.

Place the eggs in a saucepan of cold water and bring slowly to a boil over medium heat. Reduce the heat and simmer for 10 minutes. Remove the eggs from the water with a slotted spoon. Crack, cool and remove the shells. Cut each egg into quarters.

Combine the vermicelli, cabbage, chicken and lamb. Place on a large serving platter. Pour over the dressing. Top with the quartered eggs and sprinkle with chives.

HINTS: Dried rice vermicelli is available from Asian speciality food stores and many supermarkets.

This is an ideal recipe for using up small amounts of leftover cooked lamb and chicken. If you cannot tolerate eggs, simply omit them.

Browning meat, broiling (grilling), barbecuing or charring will increase natural amine levels, so poach, bake or steam meats where possible.

stuffed pear salad

Low chemical.
Contains nuts and egg. Free of dairy, gluten and soy.

4–6 (2 lb 4 oz/1 kg) small ripe pears

⅓ cup (85 g) drained, chopped canned pears

⅓ cup (45 g) chopped celery

⅓ cup (50 g) chopped cashews

¼ cup (60 ml) Salad Dressing (see Basics)

⅓ cup (90 g) Mayonnaise (see Basics)

4 large iceberg lettuce leaves, shredded

finely chopped fresh chives, for garnish

3 hard-boiled eggs, yolk only, finely chopped

Prep time: 35 minutes

Cooking time: Nil

Serves 4–6

Cut off the top part of the fresh pears closest to the stem, about one-quarter down the pear. Carefully remove the cores from the pears using a teaspoon or melon baller.

Put the chopped canned pears, celery, cashews and salad dressing in a bowl and mix together. Fill each pear with some of the mixture. Top with a spoonful of the mayonnaise.

Cover a serving plate with shredded lettuce, then put the pears on top. Garnish with chives and egg yolk. Place the top of pear to the side of the filled pear. Refrigerate until chilled, then serve.

HINT: Use small ripe pears with unblemished skin. For the best results, try to choose pears of equal size.

Manufacturers can sometimes change product ingredients. Always read the product labels to check for possible changes.

glazed drumsticks

Low chemical.
Free of egg, dairy, gluten, nut and soy.

8 (2 lb 12 oz/1.25 kg) large
chicken drumsticks
(skin removed)

⅓ cup (80 ml) golden syrup

¼ cup (60 ml) Pear Juice
(see Basics)

1 tablespoon canola oil

1 teaspoon ground sea salt

Prep time: 20 minutes +
overnight marinating time

Cooking time: 40 minutes

Serves 4

Put the drumsticks in a shallow non-metallic dish. Combine the remaining ingredients and pour over the drumsticks, making sure all are coated. Marinate overnight, turning occasionally.

Preheat the oven to 350°F (180°C/Gas 4). Put the drumsticks and marinade into a baking dish. Bake for 35–40 minutes, turning frequently during cooking and brushing with the pan juices. If the pan juices start to overbrown, add a small amount of water or stock until syrupy. Serve hot or cold.

glazed chicken with garlic and poppy seeds

Low chemical.
Free of egg, dairy, gluten, nut and soy.

For added flavor, add 2 finely chopped scallions (spring onions), 2 crushed garlic cloves and 1 tablespoon poppy seeds to the golden syrup marinade. Follow the same method.

The key to successfully
following any eating plan is
to avoid boredom — variety
really is the spice of life.
With that in mind,
there are dishes here
to feed the family, as
well as special occasion
recipes that would be
ideal for entertaining.
You won't feel at all
restricted by the
limitations of your diet
when you consider the many
delicious options available
in this chapter.

main courses

hamburgers

Low chemical.
Free of egg, dairy, gluten, nut and soy.

1 lb 2 oz (500 g) ground (minced) veal

4 scallions (spring onions), finely chopped

¼ cup (15 g) finely chopped fresh chives

1 garlic clove, crushed

1 egg, or equivalent egg substitute

1¼ cups (25 g) puffed rice, finely crushed

¼ cup (60 ml) water

ground sea salt

canola oil, for frying

12 slices gluten-free bread

2 tablespoons dairy-free margarine

½ head iceberg lettuce, washed, dried and shredded

Pear Chutney (see Basics)

Prep time: 30 minutes
Cooking time: 20 minutes
Makes 6 hamburgers

Combine the ground veal, scallions, chives, garlic, egg, puffed rice and water in a large bowl. Season with a pinch of salt. Using your hands, knead the mixture until well combined. Divide the veal mixture into six portions. Roll into balls, then flatten to ¼ in (5 mm) thick burgers. Heat the oil in a large frying pan over medium heat, add the burgers and cook for about 4–6 minutes on each side, or until cooked through and lightly browned.

Use a large cookie (biscuit) cutter to cut the bread into rounds. Otherwise, leave the slices square. Spread one side of each bread slice with margarine and broil (grill) spread side up for 1–2 minutes, or until crisp and golden brown.

Place a burger and lettuce between two slices of toasted bread. Serve topped with a dollop of pear chutney.

HINTS: You can make your own ground (minced) veal by buying lean veal steaks and grinding them yourself in a food processor. This is a good way to control the amount of fat that is in the meat—many pre-prepared ground meats are quite fatty.

marinated lamb kebabs

Low chemical.
Free of egg, dairy, gluten, nut and soy.

1 lb 2 oz (500 g) lamb fillet, shoulder or backstrap, cut into bite-sized cubes

4 canned pear halves

½ teaspoon citric acid

1 tablespoon golden syrup

1 tablespoon water

1½ cups (300 g) white long-grain rice

iceberg lettuce leaves, to serve

2 tablespoons finely chopped fresh chives

Prep time: 5 minutes + 2 hours marinating

Cooking time: 10 minutes

Makes 8 kebabs

Put the lamb in a non-metallic bowl. Blend the pear halves, citric acid, golden syrup and water in a food processor or blender until puréed. Pour over the lamb cubes and marinate for at least 2 hours. Soak eight bamboo skewers in water for 30 minutes.

Bring a large saucepan of water to a boil. Add the rice and cook for 12 minutes, stirring occasionally. Drain well.

Meanwhile, thread the lamb evenly onto the skewers. Barbecue or cook under a preheated broiler (grill) for 5–10 minutes, turning and brushing occasionally with the marinade until cooked as desired.

Serve the kebabs on a bed of lettuce and sprinkle with chives. Serve with the rice. These are also good served with lentils.

HINT: If you're cutting the lamb into cubes yourself, use a sharp knife to try to get the cubes as close as possible to being uniform in size—it means all the pieces will cook in the same time.

lamb kebabs with papaya marinade

Moderate chemical.
Free of egg, dairy, gluten, nut and soy.

Papaya and pawpaw contain an enzyme that will break down meat fibers and tenderize it, which makes them ideal in marinades. Use half a small papaya instead of the pear halves in the marinade.

chicken and vegetable pasta

Low chemical.
Free of egg, dairy, gluten, nut and soy.

3 (1 lb 2 oz/500 g) small, single chicken breast fillets

1½ tablespoons canola oil

1 large leek, halved lengthways, washed and thinly sliced

2 garlic cloves, crushed

5½ oz (150 g) green beans, diagonally sliced into 1¼ in (3 cm) pieces

2 celery stalks, trimmed and sliced

1 cup (250 ml) Chicken Stock (see Basics)

10½ oz (300 g) dried rice pasta spirals

ground sea salt

Prep time: 15 minutes
Cooking time: 25 minutes
Serves 4

Heat a large non-stick frying pan over medium heat. Brush the chicken with 2 teaspoons of the oil. Cook the chicken breast fillets for 4 minutes on each side, or until cooked through. Transfer to a plate, cover loosely with foil and set aside.

Heat the remaining oil in the same pan over medium heat. Add the leek and cook, stirring often, for 6–7 minutes, or until almost soft. Add the garlic, beans and celery. Cook for 2–3 minutes, or until the vegetables are tender and crisp. Increase the heat to high and pour in the stock. Simmer for 2–3 minutes, or until the liquid reduces slightly.

Meanwhile, cook the pasta following the packet instructions until *al dente*. Drain and return to the pan.

Slice the chicken across the grain. Add to the pasta along with the vegetables and sauce. Season to taste with salt. Toss until well combined. Serve immediately.

HINT: If you can tolerate gluten, make this dish with regular pasta spirals.

pasta with chicken and asparagus

Moderate chemical.
Free of egg, dairy, gluten, nut and soy.

For the less sensitive, replace the celery with 1 small bunch (5½ oz/150 g) asparagus, trimmed and sliced into 1¼ in (3 cm) pieces.

saffron chicken and rice

Low chemical.
Free of egg, dairy, gluten, nut and soy.

6 (1 lb 7 oz/650 g) chicken thigh fillets

1 tablespoon canola oil

1 tablespoon dairy-free margarine

5 scallions (spring onions), chopped

2 garlic cloves, crushed

¼ teaspoon saffron threads

2 cups (400 g) white long-grain rice

3¼ cups (810 ml) Chicken Stock (see Basics)

ground sea salt

Prep time: 20 minutes
Cooking time: 35 minutes
Serves 4–6

Cut the chicken into 1¼ in (3 cm) pieces. Heat the oil and margarine in a large heavy-based saucepan over medium–high heat. Brown the chicken on all sides. Remove from the pan and set aside.

Reduce the heat to medium. Add the scallions, garlic and saffron to the same saucepan and stir for 1 minute. Add the rice, stirring until the rice is coated with the oil.

Pour in the chicken stock, add a little salt and bring to a boil. Reduce the heat to very low, put the lid on the saucepan and cook, without lifting the lid, for 15 minutes.

Put the chicken pieces on top of the rice mixture. Do not stir. Cover with a lid and cook for a further 10 minutes, or until the chicken is cooked through. Fork the chicken through the rice. Leave to stand, covered, for a further 5 minutes before serving.

HINT: Crush the saffron threads gently between your fingers before using.

crunchy coated chicken

Low chemical.
Contains dairy. Free of egg, gluten, nut and soy.

canola oil, for greasing

10 (4 lb 8 oz/2 kg) chicken pieces, skin removed

½ cup (75 g) soy-free, gluten-free all-purpose (plain) flour

2 eggs, or equivalent egg substitute

2 tablespoons water

1 cup (90 g) rice bran

2–3 tablespoons poppy seeds

ground sea salt

canola oil spray

CHIVE YOGURT

½ cup (125 g) natural yogurt

2 tablespoons finely chopped fresh chives

ground sea salt

Prep time: 20 minutes + 30 minutes refrigeration

Cooking time: 30 minutes

Serves 4

Preheat the oven to 400°F (200°C/Gas 6). Lightly grease a baking tray.

Dust the chicken pieces lightly with the flour. Dip in the combined egg and water, then roll in the combined bran, poppy seeds and a little salt, pressing the mixture on firmly. Put the chicken pieces on the prepared tray and refrigerate for 30 minutes to firm the coating.

Spray the chicken all over with oil spray. Bake for about 30 minutes, or until golden brown and cooked through when tested.

Meanwhile, for the chive yogurt, combine the yogurt and chives in a small bowl, then season to taste with salt.

Serve the chicken hot or cold with the chive yogurt and a salad.

extra crunchy chicken with chive mayonnaise

Low chemical.
Contains nuts and egg. Free of dairy, gluten and soy.

If you can tolerate nuts, you can add extra crunch to the coating by adding ¼ cup (40 g) finely chopped cashews to the bran mixture. And if you would prefer a non-dairy sauce for your chicken, simply stir 2 tablespoons finely chopped fresh chives into Mayonnaise (see Basics) for a delicious dairy-free alternative.

crispy fish and lentils

Low chemical.
Free of egg, dairy, gluten, nut and soy.

⅓ cup (55 g) soy-free, gluten-free all-purpose (plain) flour

ground sea salt

4 (1 lb 5 oz/600 g) boneless white fish fillets

2 tablespoons canola oil

4 scallions (spring onions), diagonally sliced

2 garlic cloves, crushed

2 x 14 oz (400 g) cans brown lentils, drained

9 oz (250 g) green beans, trimmed

Prep time: 10 minutes
Cooking time: 15 minutes
Serves 4

Combine the flour and salt on a plate. Coat the fish fillets in the seasoned flour, shaking off any excess. Heat 1 tablespoon of the oil in a large non-stick frying pan over medium–high heat. Add the fish and cook for 3–4 minutes on each side, or until cooked through and lightly browned—depending on the size of your frying pan you may need to cook the fish in batches.

Meanwhile, heat the remaining oil in a large saucepan. Cook the scallions and garlic for 2 minutes, or until softened. Add the lentils. Toss for a few minutes, or until the lentils are heated through.

Steam or microwave the beans for a few minutes, or until just tender.

Serve the fish with warm lentils and the green beans.

Margarines and oils are sometimes preserved with antioxidants to stop them going rancid. If you need to avoid these additives, check the labels carefully.

glazed lamb noisettes

Low chemical.
Free of egg, dairy, gluten, nut and soy.

2 teaspoons canola oil

8 small lamb noisettes

1 leek, sliced into thin strips lengthways

¾ cup (185 ml) Chicken Stock (see Basics)

½ cup (140 g) Pear Chutney (see Basics)

2 teaspoons maize cornstarch (cornflour) blended with 1 tablespoon water

Prep time: 10 minutes
Cooking time: 40 minutes
Serves 4

Heat the oil in a frying pan over medium heat. Add the noisettes and cook, turning often, for 15–20 minutes, or until cooked to your liking. Remove from the pan and keep warm.

Cook the leek in the same pan over medium heat for 8–10 minutes, or until tender, then remove from the pan.

Remove any fat from the pan and pour in the chicken stock. Bring to a boil and boil for 5 minutes, then reduce the heat. Add the chutney and stir until well combined. Stir in the cornstarch and water mixture and bring to a boil. Reduce the heat and simmer for a few minutes until the sauce thickens. Stir in the leeks and heat through.

Serve the leek sauce with the noisettes.

HINT: Noisettes are prepared by your butcher. They are usually thick, mid-loin chops, boned and secured with twine.

tangy baked chicken and rice

Low chemical.
Free of egg, dairy, gluten, nut and soy.

2 x 2 lb 4 oz (1 kg) chickens

½ cup (125 ml) Pear Juice (see Basics)

2 garlic cloves, crushed

1½ teaspoons citric acid

1 teaspoon ground sea salt

2 tablespoons canola oil

1½ cups (300 g) white long-grain rice

9 oz (250 g) green beans, trimmed

Prep time: 25 minutes + 3–4 hours marinating

Cooking time: 30 minutes

Serves 4–6

Cut the chickens into serving size pieces and remove the skin. Put the chicken pieces in a non-metallic bowl.

To make the marinade, combine the pear juice, garlic, citric acid and salt. Pour the marinade over the chicken and turn to coat. Marinate in the refrigerator for 3–4 hours, turning two or three times.

Preheat the oven to 375°F (190°C/Gas 5). Remove the chicken from the marinade. Arrange the pieces in a single layer in one or two shallow roasting pans. Pour the oil over the chicken and roast for 25–30 minutes, brushing with the marinade during cooking.

Meanwhile, bring a large saucepan of water to a boil. Add the rice and cook for 12 minutes, stirring occasionally. Drain well.

Steam or microwave the beans for a few minutes, or until just tender.

Serve the chicken with the rice and green beans.

HINT: Small (2 lb 4 oz/1 kg) chickens are often available in twin packs at chicken speciality shops. If unavailable, use a selection of chicken pieces.

Fresh poultry is low in natural chemicals. However, amines can form as a result of protein breakdown, so always use fresh poultry within a day of purchase and avoid overcooked or processed chicken.

fish burgers

Low chemical.
Free of egg, dairy, gluten, nut and soy.

2 tablespoons canola oil

1 lb 2 oz (500 g) boneless white fish fillets

1 leek, halved lengthways, washed and chopped

2 garlic cloves, crushed

1 lb 9 oz (700 g) white-skinned potatoes, peeled and quartered

¼ cup (30 g) chopped scallions (spring onions)

ground sea salt

iceberg lettuce leaves, to serve

Pear Chutney (see Basics), to serve

Prep time: 20 minutes + 1 hour chilling
Cooking time: 25 minutes
Serves 4

Heat 2 teaspoons of the oil in a large non-stick frying pan over medium heat. Add the fish fillets and cook for 3–4 minutes on each side, or until cooked. Set aside to cool.

Flake the fish with a fork. Heat another 2 teaspoons of the oil in the same frying pan over medium heat. Cook the leek and garlic, stirring often, for 5–6 minutes, or until the leek softens. Set aside on a plate. Wipe the pan out with paper towels.

Meanwhile, put the potatoes in a large saucepan. Cover with cold water and bring to a boil. Boil for 15 minutes, or until the potatoes are tender. Drain well. Mash with a potato masher.

Combine the mashed potato, flaked fish, leek mixture and scallions in a large bowl and mix thoroughly. Season with a little salt. Shape into eight burgers and put on a plate. Cover and chill for 1 hour.

Heat the remaining oil in the frying pan over medium heat. Cook the burgers for 3–4 minutes on each side, or until light golden and heated through. Serve with lettuce and pear chutney.

If used moderately, pear chutneys and relishes can be part of a low chemical diet. It's best to make your own so you know exactly what they contain.

continental chicken sausage

Low chemical.
Free of egg, dairy, gluten, nut and soy.

1 lb 10 oz (750 g) ground (minced) chicken

2 eggs, lightly beaten, or equivalent egg substitute

1 cup (20 g) puffed rice, finely crushed

1 tablespoon finely chopped fresh chives

1 garlic clove, crushed

2 scallions (spring onions), finely chopped

1 teaspoon ground sea salt

1–1.25 liters (4–5 cups) Chicken Stock (see Basics), for cooking sausages

1 tablespoon canola oil

Prep time: 20 minutes + 1 hour refrigeration

Cooking time: 35 minutes

Serves 4

Combine the chicken, eggs, puffed rice, chives, garlic, scallions and salt in a large bowl. Using your hands, mix and knead the mixture until completely combined.

Divide the mixture into eight even portions. Using wet hands, shape each portion into a sausage shape. Put on a large plate, cover with plastic wrap and refrigerate for 1 hour.

Pour the chicken stock into a large saucepan and bring to a boil. Reduce the heat and bring to a simmer. Add the sausages to the simmering stock. Cover and cook for 20–25 minutes, or until the sausages are cooked through. Remove the sausages from the stock with a slotted spoon and drain on paper towels.

Heat the oil in a large frying pan over medium heat, add the sausages and cook, turning often until browned all over. Serve with potato salad, if desired (see Sides).

HINT: Ground (minced) chicken is available from chicken speciality shops and some supermarkets. It can be made at home by processing chicken breast or chicken thigh fillets without the bones or skin.

Most store bought sausages contain preservatives. If you know a good butcher, ask to have sausages made up to your own recipe. Avoid contamination by having the sausages made at the start of the day when the machinery is clean.

chicken and carrot sausage

Moderate chemical.
Free of egg, dairy, gluten, nut and soy.

Add 1 small peeled and finely grated carrot to the chicken mixture before dividing into portions, then proceed with the recipe.

veal rolls with leek sauce

Low chemical.
Free of egg, dairy, gluten, nut and soy.

8 (1 lb 12 oz/800 g) veal escalopes

1 celery stalk, cut into thin 2 in (5 cm) long strips

12 oz (350 g) rutabaga (swede), peeled and cut into thin 2 in (5 cm) long strips

ground sea salt

2 tablespoons maize cornstarch (cornflour)

2 tablespoons dairy-free margarine

1 cup (250 ml) Chicken Stock (see Basics)

1 leek, white part only, washed and chopped

1 tablespoon finely chopped fresh chives

Prep time: 45 minutes
Cooking time: 40 minutes
Serves 4

Put the veal between two sheets of plastic wrap, then pound very thin with a rolling pin or small meat mallet.

Divide the celery and rutabaga into eight even portions. Place a portion in the center of each escalope. Sprinkle with salt, roll up and secure with a toothpick or tie with kitchen string.

Roll the veal rolls in cornstarch until evenly coated. Melt half the margarine in a frying pan over medium–high heat, add the rolls and brown them quickly all over. Remove from the pan, then set aside. Melt the remaining margarine in the pan, add the leek and cook for 6–7 minutes, stirring, until soft. Return the rolls to the pan, pour in the stock and bring to a boil. Reduce the heat to low, cover and cook for about 30–40 minutes, or until the meat is tender.

Remove rolls and keep warm. Blend or process the stock and leek mixture until smooth. Pour the mixture into a saucepan, add chives and heat through. Pour the sauce over the veal rolls and serve with mashed potatoes and steamed red cabbage, if desired.

butternut and leek sauce

Moderate chemical.
Free of egg, dairy, gluten, nut and soy.

Add flavor to the sauce by adding 4½ oz (125 g) peeled and cubed butternut squash (pumpkin) when you add the stock.

vegetable and veal pasta

Low chemical.
Free of egg, dairy, gluten, nut and soy.

1½ tablespoons canola oil

1 leek, halved, washed and thinly sliced

3½ oz (100 g) rutabaga (swede), peeled and chopped

3½ oz (100 g) white-skinned potatoes, peeled and chopped

2 garlic cloves, crushed

14 oz (400 g) cabbage, core removed, shredded

2 tablespoons water

1 lb 2 oz (500 g) ground (minced) lean veal

2 teaspoons maize cornstarch (cornflour)

1½ cups (375 ml) Veal Stock (see Basics)

ground sea salt

13 oz (375 g) rice pasta

Prep time: 20 minutes
Cooking time: 25 minutes
Serves 4

Heat 1 tablespoon of the oil in a large non-stick frying pan over medium heat. Add the leek, rutabaga, potato and garlic. Cook, stirring often, for 5–6 minutes, or until the vegetables are almost tender. Add the cabbage and water. Cover and cook for a further 7–8 minutes, or until the cabbage is tender. Remove the vegetables from the pan.

Heat the remaining oil in the pan over high heat. Add the veal and cook, stirring, for 3–4 minutes, or until well browned. In a bowl, combine the cornstarch with a little of the stock, then add the remaining stock and a little salt. Add the stock mixture to the veal with the vegetables and stir until boiling. Reduce the heat and simmer for 2–3 minutes, or until the sauce thickens.

Meanwhile, cook the pasta following the packet instructions until *al dente*. Drain and return to the pan.

Divide the pasta among four serving plates. Top with the meat and vegetable mixture and serve immediately.

HINT: If you can tolerate gluten, both pasta sauces can also be served with wheat spaghetti or other wheat pasta.

vegetable and veal pasta with carrot

Moderate chemical.
Free of egg, dairy, gluten, nut and soy.

Replace the potato and rutabaga (swede) with 2 (7 oz/200 g) carrots, peeled and chopped into small cubes.

veal meatballs

Low chemical.
Free of egg, dairy, gluten, nut and soy.

1 lb 2 oz (500 g) ground (minced) veal

1 egg white, or equivalent egg substitute

½ cup (40 g) fresh gluten-free breadcrumbs

1 garlic clove, crushed

2 tablespoons finely chopped fresh chives

3 scallions (spring onions), finely chopped

ground sea salt

1 tablespoon canola oil

Pear Chutney (see Basics), for serving

Prep time: 25 minutes
Cooking time: 20 minutes
Serves 4–6

Combine the veal, egg white, breadcrumbs, garlic, chives, scallions and a pinch of salt in a large bowl. Using your hands, mix and knead until the mixture is completely combined. Using wet hands, roll tablespoons of the mixture into balls.

Heat the oil in a large frying pan and cook the meatballs, in batches, for 8–10 minutes, or until lightly browned all over.

Serve the meatballs with pear chutney and your choice of salad or vegetables (see Sides).

HINT: If your supermarket does not stock ground (minced) veal, ask your butcher to supply it. Alternatively, make your own by buying lean veal steak and grinding it yourself in a food processor.

tangy greek-style sauce

Low chemical.
Contains egg. Free of dairy, gluten, nut and soy.

If you can tolerate egg, you can make this sauce to serve with the meatballs. Blend 1 tablespoon maize cornstarch (cornflour) with 2 tablespoons water in a small bowl. In a separate bowl, combine ¼ cup (60 ml) Pear Juice (see Basics), ½ teaspoon citric acid and 1 egg yolk. Bring 1 cup (250 ml) Chicken Stock (see Basics) to a boil in a saucepan, remove from the heat and add the cornstarch mixture. Return to the heat and stir until the mixture boils and thickens. Remove from the heat and stir in the egg mixture. Pour over the meatballs to serve.

lamb with rutabaga purée

Low chemical.
Contains alcohol. Free of egg, dairy, gluten, nut and soy.

RUTABAGA PURÉE
1 lb 5 oz (600 g) rutabaga (swede), peeled and sliced

1 teaspoon sugar

2 tablespoons finely chopped fresh chives

2 teaspoons canola oil

1 lb 2 oz (500 g) lamb backstrap or loin fillets

¾ cup (185 ml) Chicken Stock (see Basics)

2 tablespoons gin

2 teaspoons maize cornstarch (cornflour) blended with 1 tablespoon water

Prep time: 30 minutes
Cooking time: 25 minutes
Serves 4

To make the rutabaga purée, put the rutabaga and sugar in a large saucepan. Cover with cold water. Bring to a boil, partially cover with a lid and cook over low heat until tender. Drain the rutabaga, reserving 2 tablespoons of the cooking liquid.

Meanwhile, heat the oil in a large non-stick frying pan over medium–high heat. Add the lamb and cook for 3–4 minutes on each side, or until cooked to your liking. Remove from the pan. Keep warm.

Pour the stock and gin into the frying pan, scraping any sediment into the stock. Bring to a boil and simmer for 5 minutes. Stir in the cornstarch and water mixture, add to the sauce and stir over the heat until thickened. Keep warm until ready to serve.

Purée the rutabaga and reserved cooking liquid in a food processor or blender until smooth. Stir in the chives. If you like, season with salt.

Slice the lamb on the diagonal. Place a mound of rutabaga purée on each plate. Top with the lamb and spoon on the sauce.

rice-crumbed fish with wedges

Low chemical.
Free of egg, dairy, gluten, nut and soy.

2 eggs, or equivalent egg substitute

2 tablespoons rice milk

⅓ cup (55 g) soy-free, gluten-free all-purpose (plain) flour

1 cup (75 g) rice crumbs

4 x 4½ oz (125 g) boneless white fish fillets

canola oil spray

iceberg lettuce leaves, to serve

Pear Chutney (see Basics), to serve

WEDGES

2 lb 4 oz (1 kg) white-skinned potatoes, peeled and cut into wedges

ground sea salt

canola oil spray

Prep time: 20 minutes
Cooking time: 50 minutes
Serves 4

Preheat the oven to 425°F (220°C/Gas 7). Line two large baking trays with sheets of baking paper.

Combine the egg and rice milk in a shallow dish. Put the flour and rice crumbs in separate shallow dishes. Dip the fish in flour, followed by the egg mixture and, lastly, the rice crumbs. Lay the crumbed fish in a single layer on one of the lined trays. Refrigerate until required.

Put the potato wedges in a large bowl. Sprinkle with salt. Spray the wedges with oil. Toss to coat. Spread over the other lined tray.

Bake the potato wedges for 30 minutes, turning once. Put the wedges on the lower shelf of the oven. Remove the fish from the fridge, then spray both sides of the fish lightly with oil. Add the fish to the top shelf and cook for 20 minutes, or until the fish is cooked and the wedges are crispy. Serve the fish with the wedges, lettuce and chutney.

breadcrumb-coated fish

Low chemical.
Contains egg, dairy and gluten. Free of nut and soy.

Store bought breadcrumbs are always preserved. Make your own by putting preservative-free bread slices on baking trays and baking slowly until completely crisp. Process in a food processor and store in an airtight jar. To make breadcrumb-coated fish, combine 1 egg and 1 tablespoon milk in one bowl, put ⅓ cup (55 g) all-purpose (plain) flour in a separate bowl and 2 cups (160 g) homemade breadcrumbs in a third bowl. Dip the fish first in the flour, then the egg wash, and lastly, the breadcrumbs. Cook as for Rice-crumbed Fish.

quail with poppy seed sauce

Low chemical.
Contains dairy and alcohol. Free of egg, gluten, nut and soy.

8 (3 lb 8 oz/1.6 kg) quail

ground sea salt

1 tablespoon margarine

1 tablespoon canola oil

¾ cup (185 ml) Chicken Stock (see Basics)

2 tablespoons whisky

½ cup (125 ml) cream

2 teaspoons soy-free, gluten-free all-purpose (plain) flour

2 teaspoons poppy seeds

Prep time: 15 minutes
Cooking time: 30 minutes
Serves 4

Wash the quail, then dry inside and out with paper towel. Tie the legs together with string. Season the quail lightly with salt. Heat the margarine and oil in a large deep frying pan or flameproof casserole over medium heat. Add the quail and cook until lightly browned all over.

Pour in the stock and whisky, and bring to a boil. Reduce the heat to low, add a lid and cook for 20 minutes, or until the quails are cooked through. Remove the quail and keep warm.

Blend the cream and flour together in a small bowl. Bring the stock and whisky mixture to a boil, reduce the heat and simmer rapidly for 5 minutes. Stir in the blended cream and flour and cook, stirring until the sauce has thickened; stir in poppy seeds. Serve the quail with the poppy seed sauce and vegetables of your choice.

tangy yogurt sauce

Low chemical.
Contains dairy. Free of egg, gluten, nut and soy.

For a tangy alternative, replace the cream in the poppy seed sauce with ½ cup (140 g) natural yogurt. Make sure the sauce doesn't come to a boil or it will separate.

roast chicken with potatoes

Low chemical.
Free of egg, dairy, gluten, nut and soy.

3 lb 5 oz (1.5 kg) whole chicken, rinsed and dried

canola oil, for greasing

1 tablespoon canola oil

1 tablespoon golden syrup

ground sea salt

4 (14 oz/400 g) medium floury white-skinned potatoes, peeled and halved

2 leeks, quartered lengthways and washed

Prep time: 30 minutes
Cooking time: 1½ hours
Serves 4–6

Preheat the oven to 350°F (180°C/Gas 4). Lightly grease a roasting pan.

Combine 2 teaspoons of the oil and the golden syrup in a small saucepan over medium heat and heat until warm, then brush all over the chicken. Sprinkle the chicken lightly with salt.

Put the chicken in the roasting pan and roast for 1¼–1½ hours, basting every 15 minutes. Cover the chicken with oiled foil if it starts to overbrown. Meanwhile, toss the potatoes and leeks in the remaining oil. About 45 minutes before serving time, put the vegetables around the chicken and roast, turning occasionally, until tender. The chicken is cooked when the juices run clear when a skewer is inserted into the thickest part of the thigh. Cover the chicken with foil and rest for 10 minutes before carving. Serve with the vegetables.

Try to avoid heavily flavored fats and oils, such as olive oil, corn oil, peanut oil, sesame oil, walnut oil, almond oil and solid white shortening. They all contain moderate to high levels of natural chemicals.

baked rutabaga

Low chemical.
Free of egg, dairy, gluten, nut and soy.

Add 7 oz (200 g) peeled, roughly chopped rutabaga (swede) to the roasting pan at the same time as you add the potato and leek.

baked butternut squash

Moderate chemical.
Free of egg, dairy, gluten, nut and soy.

Add 7 oz (200 g) peeled wedges of butternut squash (pumpkin) to the roasting pan at the same time as you add the potato and leek.

roast chicken with stuffing

Low chemical.
Free of egg, dairy, gluten, nut and soy.

3 lb 5 oz (1.5 kg) whole chicken

2 teaspoons canola oil

1 tablespoon golden syrup

ground sea salt, extra

RICE STUFFING

¾ cup (140 g) cooked white rice

¼ cup (15 g) finely chopped fresh chives

2 teaspoons poppy seeds

1 tablespoon dairy-free margarine

3 scallions (spring onions), finely chopped

1 garlic clove, crushed

ground sea salt

Prep time: 30 minutes

Cooking time: 1½ hours

Serves 4

Preheat the oven to 350°F (180°C/Gas 4). Lightly oil a roasting pan. Prepare the chicken by removing the neck, rinsing out the cavity with cold water, and patting dry with paper towels.

To make the stuffing, combine the rice, chives and poppy seeds in a bowl. Melt the margarine in a small frying pan over medium heat, add the scallions and garlic and cook, stirring, for 3–4 minutes, or until softened. Add to the rice mixture and mix well; season with salt. Spoon the stuffing into the chicken cavity. Close the cavity using poultry pins or by tying the legs together with string. Tuck the neck flap underneath.

Combine the oil and golden syrup in a small saucepan and heat until warm, then brush all over the chicken. Sprinkle lightly with salt.

Put the chicken in the roasting pan and roast for 1¼–1½ hours, basting every 15 minutes with the pan juices. Cover with oiled foil if the chicken starts to overbrown. It is cooked when the juices run clear when a skewer is inserted into the thickest part of the thigh. Rest for 10 minutes before carving. Serve the chicken and stuffing with roast potatoes, if desired.

butternut and breadcrumb stuffing

Moderate chemical.
Free of egg, dairy, gluten, nut and soy.

Melt 2 teaspoons dairy-free margarine in a small frying pan over medium heat, add 2 finely chopped scallions (spring onions) and 1 crushed garlic clove; cook, stirring, until softened. Combine 1 cup (80 g) fresh gluten-free breadcrumbs (see Breadcrumb-coated fish on page 102 for a recipe) and ½ cup (60 g) finely grated butternut squash (pumpkin) in a bowl. Add the scallion mixture and salt.

fish pie

Low chemical.
Free of egg, dairy, gluten, nut and soy.

3 oz (80 g) dairy-free margarine

¼ cup (40 g) soy-free, gluten-free all-purpose (plain) flour

1¾ cups (435 ml) rice milk

1 lb 2 oz (500 g) boneless white fish fillets, cut into 1¼ in (3 cm) cubes

1 tablespoon canola oil

1 leek, halved lengthways, washed and thinly sliced

1 celery stalk, thinly sliced

2 garlic cloves, crushed

ground sea salt

¼ cup (15 g) finely chopped fresh chives

1 lb 9 oz (700 g) white-skinned potatoes, peeled and quartered

⅓ cup (80 ml) rice milk, extra

Prep time: 20 minutes
Cooking time: 40 minutes
Serves 4–6

Cheeses contain varying amounts of natural food chemicals. The tastier the cheese, the higher its chemical content will be.

Preheat the oven to 400°F (200°C/Gas 6). To make the white sauce, melt 2¼ oz (60 g) of the margarine in a saucepan over medium heat. Add the flour and cook, stirring, for 1 minute. Remove from the heat and whisk in the rice milk. Return the pan to the heat and cook, stirring, until the sauce comes to a boil. Reduce heat, add the fish and simmer for 3–4 minutes, or until the fish is just cooked. Set aside.

Heat the oil in a frying pan over medium heat. Add the leek, celery and garlic. Cook, stirring often, for 8–10 minutes, or until the leeks are very soft. Add to the white sauce along with the chives. Stir to combine. Season to taste with salt.

Meanwhile, boil or steam the potatoes for 15–20 minutes, or until tender. Drain well and return to the pan. Add the remaining margarine and the extra rice milk. Mash until smooth.

Spoon the fish mixture into a 1.75–2 liter (7–8 cup) capacity shallow ovenproof dish. Top with mashed potato. Place on a baking tray and bake for 15–20 minutes, or until the top browns slightly.

cheesy fish pie

Moderate chemical.
Contains dairy and gluten. Free of egg, nut and soy.

For a cheesy version of this pie, replace the dairy-free margarine with butter. Replace the soy-free, gluten-free all-purpose (plain) flour with ¼ cup (40 g) all-purpose (plain) flour. Replace the rice milk with cow's milk. Add ½ cup (60 g) grated mild cheese to the white sauce. Sprinkle an extra ¼ cup (30 g) grated mild cheese over the top of the pie before baking.

chicken with glazed pears

Low chemical.
Contains alcohol. Free of egg, dairy, gluten, nut and soy.

6 (2 lb 4 oz/1 kg) small single chicken breast fillets

¼ cup (40 g) soy-free, gluten-free all-purpose (plain) flour

1 tablespoon canola oil

1½ oz (40 g) dairy-free margarine

3 scallions (spring onions), finely chopped

3 pears, peeled thickly and sliced into wedges

¼ cup (60 ml) vodka

¼ cup (60 ml) Chicken Stock (see Basics)

½ teaspoon ground sea salt

¼ teaspoon saffron threads

¼ teaspoon citric acid

Prep time: 20 minutes
Cooking time: 40 minutes
Serves 6

Lightly coat the chicken with flour. Heat the oil and half the margarine in a large frying pan over medium–high heat. Add half the chicken to the pan and cook for 3–4 minutes on each side, or until cooked. Remove from the pan and repeat with the remaining chicken.

Melt the remaining margarine in the same pan over medium heat, add the scallions and fry gently without browning for 3–4 minutes, or until softened. Add the pears and fry gently for 5 minutes.

Add the vodka, chicken stock, salt, saffron, citric acid and chicken to the pan. Simmer gently for 8–10 minutes, or until the sauce has reduced by one-third and the chicken is cooked through.

Put the chicken on a serving plate, spoon over the glazed pears and a little of the sauce and serve.

Citric acid is used in these recipes, as it is more likely to be tolerated than lemon juice or vinegar.

caramelized beef and potatoes

Moderate chemical.
Free of egg, dairy, gluten, nut and soy.

1 x 4 lb 8 oz (2 kg) piece of beef round roast

8 (3 lb 8 oz/1.6 kg) medium floury white-skinned potatoes, peeled

3 leeks, washed and sliced

1 cup (250 ml) Veal or Chicken Stock (see Basics)

1 tablespoon canola oil

1 teaspoon ground sea salt

2 tablespoons soft brown sugar

9 oz (250 g) green beans, trimmed

Prep time: 25 minutes
Cooking time: 2¼ hours
Serves 6–8

Preheat the oven to 350°F (180°C/Gas 4). Lightly oil a roasting pan. Put the beef in the prepared pan and roast for 1 hour. Remove the beef from the oven and take out of the roasting pan.

Thinly slice the potatoes and pat dry in a cloth. Thinly slice the white and pale green part of the leeks. Put the potatoes and leeks in the roasting pan and position the beef in the center. Pour stock over the potatoes. Combine the oil, salt and brown sugar in a small bowl, then brush or rub the beef with the mixture.

Return the beef and vegetables to the oven and cook for a further 1–1¼ hours. Remove the beef. Stand for 10 minutes, then carve.

Steam or microwave the beans for a few minutes, or until just tender.

Serve the beef and potatoes with the beans and, if you like, pan juices.

HINTS: If the beef looks as though it is drying out during cooking, cover it with greased aluminium foil.

The older the beef, the more amines it contains. If you have an obliging butcher, ask for a piece of yearling, which comes from a young beast, and contains fewer chemicals than older beef.

Buy and eat meat on the day of purchase or freeze it for no more than 3–4 weeks. The older the meat, the more chance there is that high amine levels will have developed.

lamb and celery satay

Low chemical.
Contains nuts. Free of egg, dairy, gluten and soy.

1½ cups (300 g) white long-grain rice

2 tablespoons cashew paste

1 teaspoon ground sea salt

1 teaspoon sugar

¼ teaspoon citric acid

2 tablespoons Pear Juice (see Basics)

2½ tablespoons canola oil

1 lb 2 oz (500 g) lamb backstrap or loin fillets, thinly sliced

1 garlic clove, crushed

2 celery stalks, trimmed and sliced

4 scallions (spring onions), diagonally sliced

Prep time: 35 minutes
Cooking time: 20 minutes
Serves 4

Bring a large saucepan of water to a boil. Add the rice and cook for 12 minutes, or until tender, stirring occasionally. Drain and keep warm.

Put the cashew paste, salt, sugar, citric acid and pear juice in a small bowl and mix together well.

Heat half the oil in a wok or large frying pan over high heat. Stir-fry the lamb in several batches until lightly browned all over. Remove from the wok and set aside. Heat the remaining oil in the wok over medium–high heat, add the garlic and celery and stir-fry for 1 minute.

Return the lamb and any juices to the pan. Add the scallions and combined cashew paste mixture. Toss well to combine and heat through. Serve immediately with the boiled rice.

HINT: The lamb will be easier to slice thinly if it has been wrapped in plastic wrap and frozen for 30 minutes.

Boiled rice should always be eaten on the day it is cooked, otherwise bacteria can multiply and produce toxins, which may upset your stomach.

lamb and vegetable satay

Moderate chemical.
Contains nuts. Free of egg, dairy, gluten and soy.

For the less sensitive, add 2 (7 oz/200 g) peeled and thinly sliced carrots to the pan with the celery and garlic.

chickpea fritters

Low chemical.
Free of egg, dairy, gluten, nut and soy.

2 tablespoons canola oil

4 scallions (spring onions), sliced

2 garlic cloves, chopped

2 x 10½ oz (300 g) cans chickpeas, rinsed and drained

ground sea salt

1 egg, or equivalent egg substitute

Pear Chutney (see Basics), to serve

iceberg lettuce, to serve

gluten-free bread, to serve

Prep time: 20 minutes
Cooking time: 10 minutes
Makes 6 fritters

Heat 2 teaspoons of the oil in a large non-stick frying pan over medium heat. Add the scallions and garlic and cook, stirring, for 1–2 minutes, or until the scallions soften.

Put the chickpeas, scallion mixture and a little salt in the bowl of a food processor. Process until the mixture starts to hold together. Transfer to a bowl and mix in the egg. Using your hands, shape the mixture into six even fritters.

Heat the remaining oil in a large non-stick frying pan over medium heat. Add the chickpea fritters (cook in two batches if necessary) and cook for 2 minutes on each side, or until golden. Serve with chutney, lettuce and crusty gluten-free bread.

lamb fillet with pea sauce

Moderate chemical.
Free of egg, dairy, gluten, nut and soy.

2 tablespoons canola oil

1 lb 12 oz (800 g) lamb fillets

1 garlic clove, peeled and slivered

PEA SAUCE

1 cup (155 g) frozen peas

¼ cup (15 g) parsley, chopped

3 scallions (spring onions), chopped

¼ cup (60 ml) Pear Juice (see Basics)

¼ teaspoon citric acid

¼ cup (60 ml) Chicken Stock (see Basics)

Prep time: 25 minutes

Cooking time: 15 minutes

Serves 4

Preheat the oven to 350°F (180°C/Gas 4). Heat the oil in a roasting pan. Add the lamb fillets and garlic to the roasting pan. Bake for 8–10 minutes for medium or 12–15 minutes for well done.

While the lamb is cooking, prepare the pea sauce. Bring a small saucepan of water to a boil, add the peas, parsley and scallions and cook for 2 minutes, or until the peas are bright green and tender. Drain, reserving ⅓ cup (80 ml) of the cooking liquid. Purée the peas, reserved liquid, pear juice, citric acid and stock in a food processor or blender. Return the purée to the saucepan and heat over low heat until the sauce is heated through.

Remove the lamb from the oven. Slice and arrange on serving plates. Spoon the pea sauce to the side. If desired, serve potatoes cooked by the method of your choice.

chinese-style chicken noodles

Low chemical.
Free of egg, dairy, gluten, nut and soy.

8 (1 lb 15 oz/880 g) chicken thigh fillets

⅓ cup (80 ml) canola oil, plus extra, for deep-frying

¼ cup (60 ml) Pear Juice (see Basics)

1 tablespoon chopped fresh chives

1 tablespoon citric acid

1 teaspoon ground sea salt

9 oz (250 g) dried rice vermicelli

1 cup (125 g) maize cornstarch (cornflour)

2 eggs, lightly beaten, or equivalent egg substitute

Prep time: 25 minutes + 1 hour marinating
Cooking time: 25 minutes
Serves 4–6

Cut the chicken thigh fillets into thin strips and put in a non-metallic bowl. Combine the oil, pear juice, chives, citric acid and salt in a small bowl. Pour over the chicken, cover and marinate for 1 hour.

Put the dried rice vermicelli in a bowl. Cover with cold water and soak for 5–10 minutes, or until soft and pliant.

Meanwhile, drain the chicken and toss in the cornstarch to give a light coating. Dip in beaten egg.

Fill a wok or deep-fat fryer one-third full of oil and heat to 350°F (180°C), or until a cube of bread dropped in the oil browns in 15 seconds. Deep-fry the chicken in small batches for about 5 minutes, or until cooked through and golden brown. Drain on paper towel and keep warm while you cook the rest.

Drain the noodles. Using a clean wok, add 2 tablespoons of oil, add the noodles and stir over high heat for 2–3 minutes. Place the noodles onto a serving platter. Top with the chicken to serve.

chinese-style chicken and vegetables with noodles

Moderate chemical.
Free of egg, dairy, gluten, nut and soy.

For a truly Chinese-style meal, before frying the softened noodles, stir-fry (in the following order), ½ cup (60 g) chopped green beans, 2 chopped celery stalks, 4 scallions (spring onions), sliced diagonally, ¼ small cabbage, shredded, and half a bunch of pak choi (bok choy), roughly chopped. Add the softened noodles and stir to combine, before serving with the prepared chicken.

soy cashew loaf

Low chemical.
Contains nuts, dairy and soy. Free of egg and gluten.

canola oil, for greasing

4 cups (800 g) cooked soy beans, drained

2 cups (310 g) raw cashews

2 tablespoons canola oil

4 scallions (spring onions), finely chopped

1 garlic clove, crushed

4 celery stalks, finely chopped

3 tablespoons poppy seeds

2 eggs, or equivalent egg substitute

ground sea salt

YOGURT AND CHIVE SAUCE

7 oz (200 g) natural yogurt

2 tablespoons finely chopped fresh chives

1 scallion (spring onion), finely chopped

ground sea salt

Prep time: 25 minutes
Cooking time: 1 hour 25 minutes
Serves 6

Preheat the oven to 325°F (170°C/Gas 3). Lightly grease a 5½ × 8½ in (14 × 21 cm) loaf pan with canola oil. Blend or process the soy beans and cashews to a coarse paste.

Heat the oil in a frying pan, add the scallions, garlic and celery and cook, stirring until soft but not browned. Combine the poppy seeds, soy bean mixture, eggs and scallion mixture in a large bowl, mix well and season with salt.

Press the mixture into the prepared loaf pan and bake for 1¼ hours, or until cooked through. Rest for 15 minutes.

Meanwhile, for the yogurt and chive sauce, combine the yogurt, chives, scallion and salt to taste in a small bowl.

Cut the loaf into thick slices (taking care as it may crumble slightly) and serve warm or cold with a dollop of the sauce.

HINT: Soy beans are a highly nutritious, complete protein food. Canned soy beans can be used in this recipe, although they may be difficult to find. If using dry beans you will need to soak 1½ cups (275 g) soy beans overnight in plenty of cold water. Drain, place in a large saucepan and cover with cold water, bring to a boil and cook for 1 hour, or until tender.

chicken and pasta salad

Moderate chemical.
Contains egg. Free of dairy, gluten, nut and soy.

3 cups (750 ml) Chicken Stock (see Basics)

14 oz (400 g) chicken breast fillets

9 oz (250 g) dried rice pasta shells

3½ oz (100 g) snow peas (mangetout) or green beans, halved

½ cup (80 g) frozen green peas

1 Golden Delicious apple, peeled, cut into thin wedges

3 eggs

DRESSING

½ cup (125 g) Mayonnaise (see Basics)

3 tablespoons finely chopped fresh chives

1 tablespoon water

ground sea salt

Preparation time: 20 minutes
Cooking time: 20 minutes
Serves 4

Bring the chicken stock to a boil in a saucepan. Remove from the heat, add the chicken to the stock, then cover and allow to cool in the liquid. Take care not to allow the chicken to boil in the liquid or it will become tough and dry. After about 10 minutes, the chicken should be cooked (this time may vary by 1–2 minutes). Cool slightly, then slice the chicken thinly across the grain.

Meanwhile, cook the pasta following the packet instructions until *al dente*. Drain, then cool under cold water. Drain again.

Boil, steam or microwave the snow peas or green beans until just tender. Refresh under cold water, then drain.

Bring a small saucepan of water to a boil, add the frozen peas and cook for 2 minutes, or until bright green and tender. Drain well, then refresh under cold water.

Place the eggs in a saucepan of cold water and bring slowly to a boil over medium heat. Reduce the heat and simmer for 10 minutes. Remove the eggs from the water with a slotted spoon. Crack, cool and remove the shells. Cut each egg into quarters.

For the dressing, combine the mayonnaise, chives and water in a small bowl, then season to taste with salt.

Combine the chicken, pasta, snow peas or beans, peas, apple and egg in a large bowl. Add the dressing and toss gently to combine.

When you are restricting your diet because of food intolerance, it can sometimes become difficult to keep your meals nutritionally balanced. But you can say goodbye to boring old meat and steamed vegetables. This chapter will inspire you with lots of great ideas for keeping the variety in your meals with deliciously different ways to serve vegetables, interesting salads and tasty purées and sauces.

sides

carrot and potato purée

Moderate chemical.
Free of egg, dairy, gluten, nut and soy.

1 tablespoon dairy-free margarine

1 tablespoon canola oil

1 lb 2 oz (500 g) carrots, peeled and chopped

2 garlic cloves, crushed

1 lb 2 oz (500 g) white-skinned potatoes, peeled and chopped

1 cup (250 ml) Vegetable Stock (see Basics)

finely chopped fresh chives, to serve (optional)

Prep time: 15 minutes
Cooking time: 25 minutes
Serves 4–6

Heat the margarine and oil in a large frying pan over medium heat. Add the carrots and garlic and cook, stirring often, for 10 minutes, or until the carrots are golden. Add the potatoes and toss to coat.

Pour the stock over the vegetables. Cover and bring to a boil. Reduce the heat to low and cook, covered, for 10–15 minutes, or until the vegetables are very tender. Set aside for 5 minutes to cool.

Put the vegetables and any liquid into the bowl of a food processor. Process until almost smooth. Scoop into a serving bowl and garnish with a sprinkle of chopped chives, if desired.

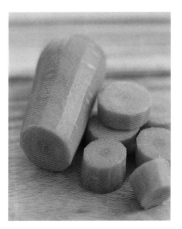

creamy rutabaga purée

Low chemical.
Contains dairy. Free of egg, gluten, nut and soy.

1 lb 5 oz (600 g) rutabaga (swedes), peeled and thickly sliced

1 teaspoon sugar

2 tablespoons cream

ground sea salt

Prep time: 15 minutes
Cooking time: 20 minutes
Serves 4–6

Put the rutabaga and sugar in a saucepan and cover with cold water. Cover and bring to a boil. Reduce the heat to low and cook, covered, for 10–15 minutes, or until the rutabaga is tender. Drain and set aside for 5 minutes to cool.

Put the rutabaga into the bowl of a food processor. Process until smooth. Stir in the cream and season with salt to taste.

pea purée with yogurt

Moderate chemical.
Contains dairy. Free of egg, gluten, nut and soy.

2 cups (310 g) frozen peas

¼ cup (15 g) parsley, chopped

6 scallions (spring onions), chopped

½ cup (125 ml) Pear Juice (see Basics)

½ teaspoon citric acid

1 cup (280 g) natural yogurt

Prep time: 10 minutes
Cooking time: 5 minutes
Serves 4

Bring a saucepan of water to a boil, then add the peas, parsley and scallions. Cook for 2–3 minutes, or until the peas are bright green and tender.

Strain, and reserve ⅓ cup (80 ml) of the cooking liquid. Purée the peas, reserved cooking liquid, pear juice and citric acid in a food processor or blender. Return to the saucepan and cook over low heat until the sauce is warmed through. Remove the pan from the heat and stir in the yogurt. Do not reheat once you have added the yogurt or the purée will curdle.

sugar-glazed potato

Low chemical.
Free of egg, dairy, gluten, nut and soy.

1 lb 2 oz (500 g) small, old white-skinned potatoes, peeled and chopped

2 tablespoons canola oil

2 tablespoons sugar

ground sea salt

Prep time: 15 minutes
Cooking time: 20 minutes
Serves 4

Bring a saucepan of water to a boil. Cook the potatoes for about 10 minutes, or until just tender; drain.

Heat the oil in a shallow frying pan large enough to fit the potatoes in a single layer. Add the sugar and stir over low heat until golden brown. Add the potatoes and cook until evenly coated with the glaze and heated through. Shake the pan regularly to prevent the potatoes sticking to the pan and the sugar burning. Sprinkle with salt and serve.

HINT: Potatoes taste and look great with this caramel coating—an excellent accompaniment to any baked meat.

sugar-glazed sweet potato

Moderate chemical.
Free of egg, dairy, gluten, nut and soy.

Replace the potato with the same amount of peeled and chopped sweet potato. Alternatively, use half of each.

saucy brussels sprouts

Low chemical.
Free of egg, dairy, gluten, nut and soy.

I lb 2 oz (500 g) even-sized
Brussels sprouts

2 celery stalks, sliced

SAUCE

I tablespoon dairy-free
margarine

2 scallions (spring onions),
chopped

I tablespoon maize
cornstarch (cornflour)

I cup (250 ml) rice milk

ground sea salt

Prep time: 15 minutes
Cooking time: 20 minutes
Serves 4–6

Preheat the oven to 350°F (180°C/Gas 4). To prepare the Brussels sprouts, remove any faded or wilted outer leaves and trim the stems level with the base. If the sprouts are large, cut a cross in the base to ensure even cooking. Bring a saucepan of water to a boil, add the Brussels sprouts and simmer for 5–8 minutes, or until just tender. Add the celery for the last minute of cooking. Drain the sprouts and celery.

For the sauce, melt the margarine in a frying pan over low heat. Add the scallions and cook for 1–2 minutes, or until soft. Do not allow the scallions to brown. Add the cornstarch and cook, stirring, for 1 minute. Gradually add the rice milk and cook over medium heat until the mixture boils and thickens. Add salt to taste.

Put the vegetables in a small shallow casserole dish. Pour the sauce over the top. Put the casserole dish in the oven for 3–4 minutes before serving. Serve while hot.

creamy cashew sauce

Low chemical.
Contains nuts and dairy. Free of egg, gluten and soy.

Use skim or full cream cow's milk instead of the rice milk. If you can tolerate nuts, sprinkle the top with ½ cup (75 g) chopped cashews before putting the casserole dish in the oven.

savory potato squares

Low chemical.
Contains egg. Free of dairy, gluten, nut and soy.

1 lb 2 oz (500 g) white-skinned potatoes, peeled

5 eggs, lightly beaten

2 tablespoons finely chopped fresh chives

2 scallions (spring onions), finely chopped

¼ cup (60 ml) canola oil

¾ cup (115 g) soy-free, gluten-free all-purpose (plain) flour

ground sea salt

Prep time: 20 minutes
Cooking time: 40 minutes
Serves 4–6

Preheat the oven to 350°F (180°C/Gas 4). Lightly oil a 6 x 11 in (15 x 28 cm) shallow baking tin.

Coarsely grate the potatoes into a large bowl. Add the eggs, chives, scallions and oil, then mix well.

Stir in the sifted flour and add a pinch of salt. Spoon the mixture into the prepared tin. Spread the mixture out evenly.

Bake the potato mixture for 30–40 minutes, or until cooked and golden brown. Cut into squares and serve hot or cold.

HINT: Rinse the potatoes in cold water and dry on paper towels before using. Do not grate them until you're ready to use them.

potato and cottage cheese squares

Low chemical.
Contains egg and dairy. Free of gluten, nut and soy.

For a richer flavor, add ½ cup (125 g) cottage cheese to the potato mixture at the same time as you add the eggs.

pear and bean salad

Low chemical.
Free of egg, dairy, gluten, nut and soy.

4 canned pear halves, drained
and chopped

½ cup (45 g) mung
bean sprouts

½ cup (55 g) sliced, cooked
green beans

4 scallions (spring onions),
chopped

½ cup (100 g) cooked
kidney beans

½ cup (100 g) cooked
soy beans

1 tablespoon poppy seeds

DRESSING

¼ cup (60 ml) canola oil

¾ teaspoon citric acid

½ teaspoon sugar

½ teaspoon ground sea salt

1 garlic clove, crushed

¼ cup (60 ml) water

Prep time: 15 minutes

Cooking time: Nil

Serves 4–6

Combine the pears, mung bean sprouts, green beans, scallions, kidney and soy beans in a large bowl. Mix together gently.

For the dressing, combine the oil, citric acid, sugar, salt, garlic and water. Pour over the vegetables. Chill before serving. Sprinkle with the poppy seeds just before serving.

HINT: This salad is best made the day before serving to allow full combination of flavors. Use any combination of your favorite beans.

green beans vinaigrette

Low chemical.
Free of egg, dairy, gluten, nut and soy.

1 lb 10 oz (750 g) green beans, trimmed

DRESSING

4 scallions (spring onions), white section only, chopped

¼ cup (60 ml) canola oil

¼ teaspoon citric acid

½ teaspoon ground sea salt

¼ teaspoon soft brown sugar

1 tablespoon water

Prep time: 10 minutes
Cooking time: 5 minutes
Serves 4–6

Bring a saucepan of water to a boil and cook the beans for 2 minutes, or until tender and bright green. Drain well.

For the dressing, put the scallions, oil, citric acid, salt, soft brown sugar and water in a small bowl. Mix together well. Pour the dressing over the warm beans. Cover, then refrigerate. Serve cold.

HINT: Another great way to serve beans is to soften 8 chives in boiling water, then drain. Use the chives to tie up bundles of beans. Steam the beans for 5–8 minutes, or until just tender. Sprinkle with salt and serve.

potato soufflé

Low chemical.
Contains egg. Free of dairy, gluten, nut and soy.

2 lb 4 oz (1 kg) white-skinned
old potatoes, peeled thickly
and roughly chopped

2 tablespoons canola oil

4 eggs, separated

7 fl oz (200 ml) Chicken Stock
(see Basics)

sea salt

canola oil, for greasing

½ cup (35 g) rice crumbs

Prep time: 25 minutes
Cooking time: 50 minutes
Serves 4–6

Preheat the oven to 400°F (200°C/Gas 6). Lightly oil a 1–1.5 liter (4–6 cup) soufflé dish.

Boil or steam the potatoes for about 15 minutes, or until tender. Drain well and mash with a potato masher. Add the oil, egg yolks and chicken stock. Beat with a wooden spoon and season to taste with salt.

Beat the egg whites until firm peaks form. Fold the egg whites gently into the potato mixture.

Spoon the mixture into the prepared dish and sprinkle with the rice crumbs. Bake for 30–35 minutes. Serve at once.

sweet potato soufflé

Moderate chemical.
Contains egg and dairy. Free of gluten, nut and soy.

For a change, replace half the potato with 1 lb 2 oz (500 g) sweet potato, peeled and thickly sliced. If you can tolerate dairy, replace the chicken stock with 7 fl oz (200 ml) cream.

sprout and cabbage salad

Low chemical.
Free of egg, dairy, gluten, nut and soy.

½ small (1 lb 5 oz/600 g) red cabbage, core removed, finely shredded

15 oz (420 g) can four bean mix, rinsed and drained

7 oz (200 g) mung bean sprouts

4 large scallions (spring onions), sliced

DRESSING

1 tablespoon canola oil

1 tablespoon water

¼ teaspoon citric acid

1 large garlic clove, crushed

ground sea salt

Prep time: 15 minutes

Cooking time: Nil

Serves 6

Put the shredded cabbage, four bean mix, bean sprouts and scallions in a large serving bowl. Mix together gently.

For the dressing, whisk the oil, water and citric acid together in a small bowl. Stir in the garlic. Season with salt to taste. Pour the dressing over the salad. Toss well to combine.

HINT: The cabbage can be chopped, covered with plastic wrap and refrigerated for up to 3 hours before serving.

Most fruits and many vegetables contain natural salicylates, and some also have high amine levels. In many cases these natural chemicals are concentrated near the skin and you can avoid them by peeling.

french-style potato salad

Low chemical.
Free of egg, dairy, gluten, nut and soy.

2 lb 4 oz (1 kg) white-skinned potatoes, peeled thickly

½ cup (125 ml) Salad Dressing (see Basics)

2 tablespoons finely chopped fresh chives

Prep time: 15 minutes
Cooking time: 15 minutes
Serves 4–6

Boil or steam the potatoes for 15 minutes, or until just tender. Drain and cut into large dice. Cool slightly, then add the salad dressing and chives. Toss together gently.

HINT: Choose potatoes of the same size. For quicker cooking, dice the potatoes before boiling them, but don't let them become mushy.

creamy potato salad

Low chemical.
Contains egg. Free of dairy, gluten, nut and soy.

For a more traditional potato salad, toss the cooked potatoes in ½ cup (125 g) Mayonnaise (see Basics) instead of the salad dressing.

potato and beetroot salad

Moderate chemical.
Contains dairy. Free of egg, gluten, nut and soy.

Cut off the green tops of 2 whole beetroot, leaving about 2 in (5 cm) of stem. Place in a saucepan of boiling water and cook for 20–30 minutes, or until tender. Drain. When cool enough to handle, remove and discard the skin and stem. Dice the beetroot and combine with 1 lb 2 oz (500 g) cooked potatoes just before serving (to minimize the beetroot color staining the potato). Combine ½ cup (125 g) natural yogurt and ¼ cup (15 g) finely chopped fresh chives, then toss through the beetroot and potato mixture.

french-style rice

Low chemical.
Free of egg, dairy, gluten, nut and soy.

I tablespoon canola oil

I leek, thinly sliced

I¼ cups (250 g) long-grain white rice

I teaspoon ground sea salt

2 cups (500 ml) Chicken Stock (see Basics)

2 tablespoons finely chopped fresh chives

Prep time: 10 minutes

Cooking time: 25 minutes

Serves 4–6

Heat the oil in a saucepan over medium heat and add the leek. Cook, stirring, for 3–4 minutes, or until the leek is softened.

Add the rice and cook, stirring, until the rice is golden brown. Add the salt, then pour in the chicken stock and bring to a boil. Allow the rice to boil until large tunnels appear in the surface.

Cover the saucepan and reduce the heat to very low heat. Cook, covered, for 15 minutes or until the rice is tender. Add the chives and use a fork to fluff up the rice.

HINT: One cup of raw rice will swell to 3 cups when cooked.

lebanese-style bread salad

Low chemical.
Contains egg. Free of dairy, gluten, nut and soy.

3 eggs

6 slices gluten-free bread, crusts removed, cut into 1 in (2.5 cm) cubes

2 tablespoons canola oil

2 garlic cloves, crushed

6 large iceberg lettuce leaves, torn

1 large celery stalk, thinly sliced

¼ cup (15 g) finely chopped fresh chives

DRESSING

1 tablespoon canola oil

1 tablespoon water

¼ teaspoon citric acid

Prep time: 15 minutes
Cooking time: 30 minutes
Serves 6

Preheat the oven to 400°F (200°C/Gas 6). Put the eggs in a small saucepan and cover with cold water. Bring to a boil. Simmer, partially covered, for 10 minutes. Drain and rinse under cold running water. Set aside to cool slightly. Peel the eggs and cut each egg into quarters.

Meanwhile, put the bread, oil and garlic in a bowl. Toss to combine. Spread the bread cubes in a single layer over a large baking tray. Bake for 12–15 minutes, or until golden brown. Set aside to cool.

For the dressing, whisk the oil, water and citric acid together.

Put the lettuce, celery and chives in a large serving bowl. Toss to combine. Pour the dressing over the salad and toss to coat. Top with the bread cubes and egg quarters. Serve immediately.

HINT: Store bought gluten-free bread sometimes contains soy, dairy or egg. Check the label or make your own (see page 143).

If you're highly sensitive to food chemicals, discard the darker, outer leaves of a lettuce and use only the lighter-colored inner leaves.

Store bought breads and pizzas can present a veritable minefield of food chemicals and problem ingredients, such as gluten. One way to control exactly what you're eating is to make them yourself—and you'll be surprised at how easy and satisfying it is to make your own bread. Use the recipes in this chapter as a starting point and add toppings and fillings that fit in with your own dietary guidelines.

breads & pizzas

gluten-free bread rolls

Low chemical.
Free of egg, dairy, gluten, nut and soy.

canola oil, for greasing

4 teaspoons (2 x 7 g packages) dried yeast

1 tablespoon soft brown sugar

2 cups (500 ml) warm water

2 teaspoons guar gum (from health food stores)

2 cups (300 g) soy-free, gluten-free all-purpose (plain) flour

¾ cup (130 g) rice flour

2 teaspoons ground sea salt

½ cup (45 g) rice bran

2¼ oz (60 g) dairy-free margarine, melted and cooled

2 tablespoons poppy seeds, optional

canola oil, for brushing

Prep time: 40 minutes + proving time

Cooking time: 35 minutes

Makes 8 individual loaves

The ideal temperature of a 'warm place' for dough is about 86°F (30°C)—in a sheltered sunny spot, or on top of, but not actually inside, a warm oven.

Preheat the oven to 400°F (200°C/Gas 6). Lightly grease eight 4 x 2¼ x 1½ in (10 x 5.5 x 3.5 cm) individual loaf tins.

Combine the yeast, sugar and warm water in a bowl, then stir to dissolve the yeast. Stand the bowl in a warm place for about 10 minutes, or until the mixture is frothy.

Sift the gum and flours into a large bowl. Add the salt and rice bran. Make a well in the center and add the yeast mixture and cooled margarine. Mix well to form a soft dough. Divide into eight equal portions, then gently shape with floured hands into an oval shape. Place in the prepared tins. Sprinkle with poppy seeds, if using.

Cover loosely and place in a warm place for 45–60 minutes, or until the mixture comes to the top of the tins.

Bake for 25–30 minutes, or until cooked through. Brush with oil during cooking at least twice to help promote browning. Remove from the tins and allow to cool on a wire rack.

HINT: The rolls are best eaten on the day they are made, or they can be frozen until required.

bread rolls

Low chemical.
Contains gluten. Free of egg, dairy, nut and soy.

canola oil, for greasing

4 teaspoons (2 x 7 g packages) dried yeast

1 tablespoon soft brown sugar

1¾ cups (435 ml) warm water

2¾ cups (340 g) baker's flour

2 teaspoons ground sea salt

½ cup (45 g) rice bran

2¼ oz (60 g) dairy-free margarine, melted and cooled

2 tablespoons poppy seeds, optional

Prep time: 40 minutes + proving time
Cooking time: 35 minutes
Makes 8 individual loaves

Preheat the oven to 400°F (200°C/Gas 6). Lightly grease eight 4 x 2¼ x 1½ in (10 x 5.5 x 3.5 cm) individual loaf tins.

Combine the yeast, sugar and warm water in a bowl, then stir to dissolve the yeast. Stand the bowl in a warm place for about 10 minutes, or until the mixture is frothy.

Sift the flour into a large bowl. Add the salt and rice bran. Make a well in the center and add the yeast mixture and cooled margarine. Mix well to form a soft dough. Place the dough in a large bowl, cover and leave to stand in a warm place for about 30 minutes, or until the dough has doubled in size.

Punch the dough down lightly, then divide into eight equal portions. Gently shape with floured hands into an oval shape and place in the prepared tins. Sprinkle with poppy seeds, if using.

Cover loosely and place in a warm place for about 30 minutes, or until the mixture comes to the top of the tins.

Bake for 25–30 minutes, or until cooked through. Remove from the tins and allow to cool on a wire rack.

HINT: The rolls are best eaten on the day they are made. Alternatively, they can be frozen until required.

wheatless loaf

Low chemical.
Free of egg, dairy, gluten, nut and soy.

canola oil, for greasing

4 teaspoons (2 x 7 g packages) dried yeast

1 tablespoon sugar

2½ cups (625 ml) warm water

3½ cups (525 g) soy-free, gluten-free all-purpose (plain) flour

2 teaspoons ground sea salt

⅓ cup (80 ml) canola oil

2 tablespoons roasted buckwheat, optional

2 tablespoons canola oil, extra, for glazing

Prep time: 40 minutes

Cooking time: 35 minutes

Makes 1 large loaf

Preheat the oven to 425°F (220°C/Gas 7). Lightly grease a 5½ x 8 in (14 x 20 cm) loaf tin.

Combine the yeast, sugar and warm water in a bowl, then stir to dissolve the yeast. Stand the bowl in a warm place for about 10 minutes, or until the mixture is frothy.

Sift the flour into a large bowl and add the salt. Make a well in the center and add the yeast mixture and oil. Beat well with a wooden spoon.

Pour into the prepared tin and sprinkle with buckwheat, if using. Cover loosely and place in a warm place for about 20 minutes, or until the mixture comes to the top of the tin.

Bake for 20 minutes, then reduce the heat to 400°F (200°C/Gas 6) and bake for a further 30–35 minutes, or until cooked. Brush with the extra oil during cooking at least twice to help promote browning.

HINTS: Bread is best eaten on the day of baking; alternatively, you can slice it and then freeze until required.

For a high fiber loaf, add ½ cup (45 g) rice bran with the dry ingredients.

egg bread

Low chemical.
Contains egg and dairy. Free of gluten, nut and soy.

For an enriched bread dough, add 1 egg and replace the water with 2 cups (500 ml) milk. Bring the milk just to boiling point, then remove from the heat and allow to cool to lukewarm. Add the egg to the mixture with the oil and yeast mixture.

potato and leek pizza

Low chemical.
Free of egg, dairy, gluten, nut and soy.

3 cups (450 g) soy-free, gluten-free all-purpose (plain) flour

4 teaspoons (2 x 7 g packages) dried yeast

1 teaspoon ground sea salt

1½ tablespoons canola oil

1 cup (250 ml) warm water

canola oil, for greasing

TOPPING

2 tablespoons canola oil

2 leeks, halved lengthways, washed and thinly sliced

3 garlic cloves, crushed

3 (1 lb 5 oz/600 g) white-skinned potatoes, peeled and thinly sliced

ground sea salt

2 tablespoons finely chopped fresh chives

Prep time: 1½ hours
Cooking time: 35 minutes
Serves 4

Sift the flour into a large bowl. Add the yeast and salt. Make a well in the center and add the combined oil and water. Use a wooden spoon to mix until almost combined. Use your hands to mix into a soft dough.

Turn the dough out onto a lightly floured surface and knead for 1–2 minutes, or until smooth. Place the dough in a lightly oiled bowl. Cover the bowl and set aside in a warm place for 1 hour, or until the dough has doubled in size.

Use your fist to punch the dough down, then knead until it returns to its original size. Lightly grease two 11 in (27 cm) pizza trays. Divide the dough into two portions. Roll out one portion on a lightly floured surface to fit the tray, then carefully place the dough onto the tray. Repeat with the remaining dough.

Preheat the oven to 475°F (240°C/Gas 8). For the topping, heat 1 tablespoon of the oil in a large non-stick frying pan over medium heat. Add the leeks and garlic and cook, stirring often, for 8–10 minutes, or until the leeks are very soft. Remove from the heat and set aside.

Meanwhile, steam or microwave potato slices until almost tender. Transfer to a plate lined with paper towels.

Spread half of the leek mixture over each pizza base. Arrange the potato slices in a thin layer over the leeks. Sprinkle with salt and brush with the remaining oil. Bake for 20–25 minutes, swapping the trays around once, or until the potatoes and dough are golden. Sprinkle the chives over the pizzas and serve.

HINT: Use the pizza dough as a base for other toppings.

potato rolls

Low chemical.
Free of egg, dairy, gluten, nut and soy.

canola oil, for greasing
14 oz (400 g) white-skinned potatoes, peeled and roughly chopped
1 cup (250 ml) warm water
2 teaspoons (7 g package) dried yeast
¼ cup (55 g) sugar
¼ cup (60 ml) canola oil
ground sea salt
2–2½ cups (300–375 g) potato flour
2 eggs, or equivalent egg substitute

Prep time: 1¾ hours
Cooking time: 30 minutes
Makes 18–20 rolls

Preheat the oven to 375°F (190°C/Gas 5). Lightly oil two baking trays.

Boil or steam the potatoes for 15 minutes, or until tender. Drain well, and mash until smooth. You will need 1 cup (230 g) warm mashed potato for this recipe.

In a large bowl, combine the warm water, yeast and half the sugar. Allow to stand for 10 minutes, or until frothy.

Add the oil, mashed potatoes and salt to the yeast mixture. Stir in 1 cup (150 g) of the potato flour and the remaining sugar. Beat for 1 minute with a wooden spoon. Stand in a warm place until the mixture forms a sponge. It will rise and look foamy.

Add the rest of the flour to make a firm dough. Stand in a warm place until doubled in bulk.

Turn the dough out onto a board dusted with potato flour. Using a little extra potato flour, shape the dough into rolls. Place on the prepared baking trays. Cover with plastic wrap. Stand in a warm place and let rise for 10 minutes. Brush with egg and bake for 10–12 minutes.

HINT: This dough produces a bread roll with a bagel-like crust and chewy texture. Potato rolls can be frozen. Wrap them in foil to reheat in the oven.

poppy seed rolls

Low chemical.
Free of egg, dairy, gluten, nut and soy.

Sprinkle the glazed potato bread rolls with 1 tablespoon poppy seeds.

savory flat bread

Low chemical.
Free of egg, dairy, gluten, nut and soy.

canola oil, for greasing
½ cup (70 g) brown rice flour
½ cup (50 g) arrowroot
¾ teaspoon baking soda (bicarbonate of soda)
1½ teaspoons cream of tartar
1 cup (90 g) rice bran
1 cup (250 ml) Chicken Stock (see Basics) or water
¼ cup (60 ml) canola oil
canola oil, extra, for greasing and glazing
1 tablespoon ground sea salt
1 tablespoon poppy seeds

Prep time: 20 minutes
Cooking time: 40 minutes
Makes 6–8 rounds

Preheat the oven to 375°F (190°C/Gas 5). Grease two baking trays well.

Sift the flour, arrowroot, baking soda and cream of tartar into a large bowl. Add the rice bran. Make a well in the center, then add the combined stock and oil. Beat until smooth with a wooden spoon.

Spoon heaping tablespoons of the dough onto the prepared trays.

Bake for 20 minutes. Remove from the oven, brush with oil and sprinkle with salt and poppy seeds. Return to the oven and bake for a further 15–20 minutes.

HINT: The bread can be topped or split and filled. It does not freeze well but can be kept in the refrigerator for 2–3 days.

egg flat bread

Low chemical.
Contains egg. Free of dairy, gluten, nut and soy.

Replace the canola oil with 2 egg yolks. Lightly beat them before adding them to the dry ingredients with the stock or water.

fried flat bread

Low chemical.
Free of egg, dairy, gluten, nut and soy.

¾ cup (135 g) rice flour
¾ cup (130 g) potato flour
1 teaspoon gluten-free baking powder
1 teaspoon ground sea salt
1 tablespoon canola oil
¾–1 cup (185–250 ml) warm water, approximately
canola oil, extra, for frying

Preparation time: 10 minutes
Cooking time: 30 minutes
Makes 8 rounds

Sift the rice flour, potato flour and baking powder into a large bowl. Add the salt. Make a well in the center and add the oil. Gradually stir in the water, mixing until a thick batter is formed.

Heat ½ in (1 cm) oil in a frying pan and pour in enough batter to form a round about 4–5 in (10–12 cm) across. Fry until golden brown, then turn and brown the other side. Drain on paper towels. Repeat with the remaining batter. Add more oil to the pan as needed, ensuring it is heated through before use.

HINT: Use this bread as an accompaniment to any meat or lentil dish or top with the food of your choice.

Potato flour is often preserved with sulphite, but most of it will disappear during the cooking process.

If you think your allergy or food intolerance means you can't enjoy any of the sweet foods that you love, then you're in for a pleasant surprise. In this chapter, you'll find a mouth-watering collection of cakes, cookies and muffins, all carefully devised to keep food chemicals to a minimum without compromising flavor. So put the kettle on and enjoy a delicious snack time treat.

snack time

jam cookies

Low chemical.
Free of egg, dairy, gluten, nut and soy.

dairy-free margarine or butter,
for greasing

3¼ oz (90 g) dairy-free
margarine or butter

½ cup (110 g) sugar

¾ cup (135 g) rice flour

¼ teaspoon gluten-free
baking powder

1 tablespoon water

½ cup (160 g) Pear Jam
(see Basics)

Prep time: 20 minutes

Cooking time: 15 minutes

Makes 24 cookies

Preheat the oven to 375°F (190°C/Gas 5). Lightly grease two baking trays with margarine or butter.

Use electric beaters to beat the butter and sugar until light and fluffy. Stir in the sifted rice flour and baking powder. Add the water and stir until well blended and a dough forms.

Shape the dough into walnut-sized balls, then space them out on the prepared baking trays—you should have about 24 balls.

Make an indentation in each cookie using the handle of a wooden spoon. Place ¼ teaspoon jam in each cookie. Bake for 10–15 minutes, or until light golden. Cool on wire racks.

HINT: The dough can be made ahead of time and stored in the refrigerator for 2–3 days before baking.

jam and carob cookies

Low chemical.
Contains dairy and soy. Free of egg, gluten and nut.

For a special treat add ½ cup (80 g) chopped carob chips to the dough mixture. Check whether the carob contains dairy and/or soy.

chunky rice bar cookie

Low chemical.
Free of egg, dairy, gluten, nut and soy.

dairy-free margarine or butter,
for greasing

1 cup (180 g) rice flour

2 teaspoons gluten-free
baking powder

1 cup (75 g) rolled rice

½ cup (5 g) crushed
puffed rice cereal

½ cup (115 g) soft brown sugar

½ cup (125 g) dairy-free
margarine or butter, melted

CAROB COFFEE CREAM

1 cup (125 g) pure
confectioners' (icing)
sugar, sifted

¼ cup (60 g) carob powder

1 teaspoon decaffeinated
instant coffee powder

¼ cup (60 g) dairy-free
margarine or butter

2 teaspoons water

Prep time: 10 minutes
Cooking time: 25 minutes
Makes 16 pieces

Preheat the oven to 350°F (180°C/Gas 4). Lightly grease a 9 × 12 in (20 × 30 cm) baking tin with margarine or butter.

Sift the flour and baking powder into a bowl. Add the rolled rice, puffed rice cereal and brown sugar. Mix well.

Make a well in the center and add the melted margarine. Stir until well combined. Press the mixture into the prepared baking tin. Bake for 20–25 minutes, or until golden brown. Remove from the oven and leave in the tin to cool.

For the carob coffee cream, sift the confectioners' sugar, carob and coffee into a bowl. In a separate bowl, beat the margarine until pale and fluffy. Add the sifted dry ingredients and water to the bowl. Beat on high until well combined and creamy.

Turn the bar cookie onto a flat surface. Spread with the carob coffee cream and then cut into 16 slices.

HINT: This is a firm textured bar cookie suitable for including in a packed lunch.

golden syrup bar cookie

Low chemical.
Free of egg, dairy, gluten, nut and soy.

canola oil, for greasing

3 cups (495 g) rice flour

1½ teaspoons baking soda (bicarbonate of soda)

1 cup (350 g) golden syrup

½ cup (125 ml) canola oil

1½ cups (345 g) soft brown sugar

¾ cup (185 ml) warm water

ICING

1½ cups (185 g) pure confectioners' (icing) sugar

½–1 teaspoon citric acid

cold water

Prep time: 15 minutes

Cooking time: 45 minutes

Makes about 24 pieces

Preheat the oven to 350°F (180°C/Gas 4). Lightly grease a 9 × 12 in (20 × 30 cm) baking tin, then line with baking paper.

Sift the flour and baking soda into a bowl. Put the golden syrup, oil and sugar into a saucepan. Stir over low heat until the sugar dissolves, about 3–4 minutes. Allow to cool.

Add the syrup and warm water to the dry ingredients. Stir until well combined. Pour into the prepared tin. Bake for 45 minutes, or until golden. Allow to cool in the tin for 5 minutes before turning onto a wire rack to cool completely.

For the icing, sift the confectioners' sugar into a heatproof bowl. Add the citric acid and enough cold water to make a stiff paste. Place the bowl over a saucepan of simmering water. Stir until thin enough to spread. Spread the icing over the cold bar cookie. Once the icing has set, cut into slices.

HINT: This bar cookie has a light but very moist texture. It is best eaten the day after it is made.

The amounts of chemicals present in a particular food may not be enough to cause a reaction right away. However, because one substance may be common to many different foods it can accumulate in the body and eventually cause a reaction.

gluten-free griddle cakes

Low chemical.
Contains egg. Free of dairy, gluten, nut and soy.

⅔ cup (110 g) soy-free, gluten-free all-purpose (plain) flour

½ teaspoon baking soda (bicarbonate of soda)

1 teaspoon cream of tartar

⅓ cup (30 g) rice bran

2 eggs, separated

1 cup (250 ml) water

1 tablespoon canola oil

canola oil spray, for greasing

Pear Jam (see Basics), for serving (optional)

Prep time: 15 minutes
Cooking time: 25 minutes
Makes about 24 griddle cakes

Sift the flour, baking soda and cream of tartar into a bowl. Mix in the rice bran. Make a well in the center and stir in the combined egg yolks, water and oil. Beat well until smooth.

Beat the egg whites in the small bowl of an electric mixer until stiff peaks form, then fold into the batter using a large spoon.

Spray a non-stick frying pan lightly with oil and place over medium heat. Place tablespoonfuls of the mixture in the pan, allowing room for spreading. When the mixture starts to set and bubbles burst, turn over and brown the other side. Place on a wire cake rack to cool. Repeat with the remaining mixture. Serve with pear jam, if desired.

HINT: Griddle cakes can be frozen and reheated briefly in a warm oven.

griddle cakes with pear yogurt

Low chemical.
Contains egg, dairy and gluten. Free of nut and soy.

Replace the gluten-free flour with regular all-purpose (plain) flour. You will then need ¾–1 cup (185–250 ml) of water. Serve with pear yogurt. To make it, combine 1 cup (250 g) plain yogurt, ½ peeled and chopped pear and 2 teaspoons soft brown sugar.

carob brownies

Low chemical.
Contains dairy and soy. Free of egg, gluten and nut.

canola oil, for greasing

2 eggs, or equivalent egg substitute

½ cup (90 g) rice flour

1 cup (220 g) sugar

½ cup (80 g) chopped carob chips

½ cup (120 g) soy-free carob powder

1 teaspoon natural vanilla extract

Prep time: 15 minutes
Cooking time: 20 minutes
Makes about 12 pieces

Preheat the oven to 350°F (180°C/Gas 4). Lightly grease and line a 5½ × 8 in (14 × 20 cm) loaf tin, then line with baking paper.

Beat the eggs lightly. Stir in the remaining ingredients. Spread the mixture evenly into the prepared tin. Bake for 15–20 minutes. Mark into squares while warm. If desired, ice with carob topping (below).

HINT: Most carob chips contain dairy and/or soy.

carob topping

Low chemical.
Contains dairy and soy. Free of egg, gluten and nut.

1¼ cups (200 g) carob chips

2 tablespoons butter or dairy-free margarine

Prep time: 5 minutes
Cooking time: 5 minutes

Put the carob chips and butter in a small heatproof bowl over a saucepan of simmering water. Heat until the carob is melted. Stir gently to combine. Do not overheat as it will become very thick. Spread over the cooked and cooled brownies. If you cannot tolerate the dairy in carob chips, ice the brownies with Carob Glacé Icing, on page 226, as carob powder does not contain dairy.

meringue kisses

Low chemical.
Contains egg. Free of dairy, gluten, nut and soy.

canola oil, for greasing

maize cornstarch (cornflour),
for dusting

¼ cup (60 ml) egg white
(about 2 egg whites)

⅔ cup (145 g) superfine
(caster) sugar

ground sea salt

1 teaspoon pure
confectioners' (icing) sugar

Prep time: 20 minutes

Cooking time: 40 minutes

Makes about 20 meringues

Preheat the oven to 250°F (120°C/Gas 1). Lightly grease two baking trays, then dust them lightly with cornstarch.

Combine the egg whites, superfine sugar and a pinch of salt in the small bowl of an electric mixer. Beat on high speed for 10–12 minutes. Gently fold in the confectioners' sugar.

Spoon the meringue into a piping bag fitted with a fluted tube. Pipe stars or rosettes onto the prepared trays. Bake for about 40 minutes, or until the meringues feel firm and dry. Allow to cool in the oven with the door ajar.

HINT: This is a basic meringue mixture. It makes small crisp meringues that store well in an airtight container. For best results measure your egg whites. The amount must be accurate to fully absorb the quantity of sugar.

carob meringue kisses

Low chemical.
Contains egg, dairy and soy. Free of gluten and nut.

For a special treat, meringues can also be dipped in melted carob chips and/or joined together with whipped cream. Check whether the carob chips contain dairy and/or soy.

gluten-free pear bar cookie

Low chemical.
Free of egg, dairy, gluten, nut and soy.

canola oil, for greasing

1½ cups (225 g) soy-free, gluten-free self-raising flour

½ teaspoon gluten-free baking powder

¾ cup (185 g) superfine (caster) sugar

2 eggs, or equivalent egg substitute

¼ cup (60 ml) Pear Juice (see Basics)

¼ cup (60 ml) canola oil

½ cup (125 ml) cold water

4 canned pear halves, mashed

pure confectioners' (icing) sugar, to serve

Prep time: 15 minutes

Cooking time: 35 minutes

Makes about 20 pieces

Preheat the oven to 375°F (190°C/Gas 5). Lightly grease a 7 x 11 in (18 x 28 cm) baking tin, and cover the base and two long sides with baking paper.

Sift the flour and baking powder into a bowl and add the sugar. Make a well in the center. Combine the eggs, juice, oil and water in a separate bowl. Add to the dry ingredients and mix thoroughly.

Spread half the batter into the prepared baking tin. Spread the mashed pear carefully over the top, then spoon the remaining batter gently over the pear so that it is completely covered.

Bake for about 30–35 minutes, or until golden brown. Cool slightly in the tin, then turn out onto a wire rack to cool. Dust liberally with confectioners' sugar and cut into 20 pieces before serving.

HINT: This is a moist bar cookie, best served the day it is made. Do not purée the pears—mash them with a fork.

gluten-free apple bar cookie

Moderate chemical.
Free of egg, dairy, gluten, nut and soy.

You can make this recipe into an apple bar cookie by using 1½ cups (335 g) peeled and stewed Golden Delicious apples instead of pears.

pear bar cookie

Low chemical.
Contains egg and gluten. Free of dairy, nut and soy.

canola oil, for greasing

¾ cup (185 g) superfine (caster) sugar

¾ cup (90 g) all-purpose (plain) flour

¾ cup (90 g) self-raising flour

2 eggs, lightly beaten

¼ cup (60 ml) Pear Juice (see Basics)

¼ cup (60 ml) canola oil

2 tablespoons cold water

4 canned pear halves, mashed

3 tablespoons sugar

Prep time: 15 minutes
Cooking time: 35 minutes
Makes about 20 pieces

Preheat the oven to 375°F (190°C/Gas 5). Lightly grease a 7 x 11 in (18 x 28 cm) baking tin, and cover the base and two long sides with baking paper.

Combine the dry ingredients in a bowl and make a well in the center. Combine the egg, juice, oil and cold water in a separate bowl and add to the dry ingredients. Mix until thoroughly combined.

Spread half the batter into the prepared tin. Spread the mashed pear carefully over the top, then spoon the remaining batter gently over the pear so that it is completely covered.

Bake for about 15 minutes, then sprinkle with the sugar. Bake for another 15–20 minutes, or until golden. Cool slightly in the tin, then place on a wire rack to cool.

apple bar cookie

Moderate chemical.
Contains egg and gluten. Free of dairy, nut and soy.

Replace the pears with 1½ cups (335 g) peeled and stewed Golden Delicious apples.

vanilla cookies

Low chemical.
Free of egg, dairy, gluten, nut and soy.

½ cup (125 g) dairy-free margarine

⅓ cup (80 g) superfine (caster) sugar

1 teaspoon natural vanilla extract

1 cup (150 g) soy-free, gluten-free all-purpose (plain) flour

½ cup (75 g) soy-free, gluten-free self-raising flour

Prep time: 15 minutes
Cooking time: 15 minutes
Makes about 18 cookies

Preheat the oven to 325°F (170°C/Gas 3). Line two baking trays with sheets of baking paper.

Beat the margarine, sugar and vanilla extract in the small bowl of an electric mixer for 1–2 minutes, or until well combined. Sift the flours into the margarine mixture. Use a wooden spoon to mix until well combined. Use your hands to mix to a soft dough.

Shape tablespoonsful of the mixture into balls and place on the prepared trays. Use a fork to flatten the balls until about ⅜ in (1 cm) thick. Bake for 12–15 minutes, swapping the trays around once, until light golden. Transfer cookies to a wire rack to cool.

brown sugar cookies

Low chemical.
Free of egg, dairy, gluten, nut and soy.

Replace the superfine (caster) sugar with ⅓ cup (80 g) firmly packed soft brown sugar and proceed with the basic recipe.

carob-chip cookies

Low chemical.
Contains dairy, gluten and soy. Free of egg and nut.

Replace the dairy-free margarine with butter, and the gluten-free flours with regular wheat flours (all in the same amounts). Add 3½ oz (100 g) chopped carob chips to the dough and proceed with the basic recipe. Check whether the carob chips contain dairy and/or soy.

coffee mousse meringue roll

Low chemical.
Contains egg. Free of dairy, gluten, nut and soy.

COFFEE MOUSSE

4 egg yolks

¼ cup (55 g) sugar

3 teaspoons maize cornstarch (cornflour)

1½ teaspoons decaffeinated instant coffee powder

¾ cup (185 ml) water

canola oil, for greasing

maize cornstarch (cornflour), for dusting

4 egg whites

½ cup (110 g) sugar

2 teaspoons maize cornstarch (cornflour)

pure confectioners' (icing) sugar, for dusting

Prep time: 35 minutes
Cooking time: 15 minutes
Serves 4–6

For the coffee mousse, beat the egg yolks and sugar in the small bowl of an electric mixer until thick and creamy. In a separate small bowl, blend the cornstarch, coffee powder and water. Add to the egg mixture. Transfer to a saucepan and stir over low heat until the mixture boils and thickens. Pour the mixture into a bowl. Cover with plastic wrap and chill well before using.

Preheat the oven to 400°F (200°C/Gas 6). Lightly grease a 10 × 12 in (25 × 30 cm) jelly-roll tin with canola oil, line with baking paper, grease again and dust with maize cornstarch.

Beat the egg whites until light and fluffy. Gradually beat in the sugar and continue beating until the meringue is stiff and glossy. Gently fold in the cornstarch. Spread the meringue mixture evenly into the prepared jelly-roll tin, using a spatula.

Bake for 12–15 minutes, or until the meringue has risen and is golden brown. Quickly turn out onto a sheet of baking paper that has been coated with sifted confectioners' sugar. Allow to cool until lukewarm.

Spread the chilled mousse over the meringue. Roll up from the short side using the baking paper as a guide. Place on a chilled platter. Refrigerate the roll until ready to serve, then slice.

lemon mousse

Low chemical.
Contains egg. Free of dairy, gluten, nut and soy.

Instead of coffee mousse, try this tangy filling for a change. Follow the mousse recipe, but omit coffee and use 1 teaspoon citric acid instead.

pinwheels

Low chemical.
Free of egg, dairy, gluten, nut and soy.

dairy-free margarine,
for greasing

3½ cups (525 g) soy-free,
gluten-free self-raising flour

3 teaspoons gluten-free
baking powder

ground sea salt

2¾ oz (80 g) dairy-free margarine

1 tablespoon superfine
(caster) sugar

1¼ cups (325 ml) rice milk

2 tablespoons melted
dairy-free margarine

½ cup (95 g) soft brown sugar,
plus a little extra

Prep time: 15 minutes
Cooking time: 25 minutes
Makes 12 pinwheels

Preheat the oven to 400°F (200°C/Gas 7). Lightly grease the base of an 8 in (20 cm) cake tin, then line with baking paper.

Sift the flour, baking powder and a pinch of salt into a large bowl. Use your fingertips to rub the margarine into the flour until fine crumbs form. Stir in the sugar. Add the rice milk and use a round-bladed knife to mix until the dough just comes together.

Turn out onto a lightly floured surface and knead until combined. Roll out until the dough is about ¼ in (5 mm) thick. Brush with 1 tablespoon melted dairy-free margarine. Sprinkle with the brown sugar.

Starting from one of the long sides, roll up to form a log. Trim the ends and cut into eight slices about ¾ in (2 cm) thick. Arrange over the base of the prepared pan. Brush with a little extra margarine and sprinkle with a little extra brown sugar. Bake for 20–25 minutes, or until golden.

butter pinwheels

Low chemical.
Contains dairy and gluten. Free of egg, nut and soy.

You can make these pinwheels using wheat flour, butter and milk. Replace the gluten-free flour with 3 cups (450 g) self-raising flour. Replace the margarine with butter and use 1 cup (250 ml) cow's milk instead of the rice milk.

pear puffs

Low chemical.
Contains egg. Free of dairy, gluten, nut and soy.

DAIRY-FREE CUSTARD

4 egg yolks

⅓ cup (90 g) sugar

2½ tablespoons maize cornstarch (cornflour)

¾ cup (185 ml) Pear Juice (see Basics)

¾ cup (185 ml) rice milk

½ cup (125 ml) canola oil

1½ cups (375 ml) cold water, plus a little extra

1¼ cups (190 g) soy-free, gluten-free all-purpose (plain) flour

¼ teaspoon baking soda (bicarbonate of soda)

1 teaspoon gluten-free baking powder

4 eggs

pure confectioners' (icing) sugar, to serve

Prep time: 45 minutes

Cooking time: 30 minutes

Makes 36 puffs

For the custard, beat the egg yolks and sugar in the small bowl of an electric mixer until thick and pale in color. Blend the cornstarch, pear juice and rice milk in a saucepan until smooth. Stir in the egg mixture and stir over low heat until the mixture boils and thickens. Pour into a bowl and cover the surface with plastic wrap (to prevent a skin forming). Allow to cool completely.

Preheat the oven to 415°F (210°C/Gas 6–7). Cover two baking trays with baking paper. Pour the oil and water into a saucepan and bring to a boil. Remove from the heat. Add the sifted dry ingredients, then return to the heat and stir constantly until the mixture thickens and leaves the side of the saucepan (it may look a little oily). Transfer the mixture into the small bowl of an electric mixer and allow to cool slightly.

Beat the mixture, adding the eggs one at a time and beating well between each addition until the mixture is thick and shiny.

Place level tablespoons of the mixture onto the prepared trays, then sprinkle or spray lightly all over with the extra cold water (this creates a little steam which will aid in rising).

Bake for about 10 minutes, or until they rise and start to brown. Reduce the heat to 375°F (190°C/Gas 5) and bake for 10–15 minutes, or until cooked through. Remove from the oven and allow to cool completely. Split the puffs and fill with the custard. Dust liberally with confectioners' sugar.

butternut and coconut tart

Moderate chemical.
Contains dairy. Free of egg, gluten, nut and soy.

butter or dairy-free
margarine, for greasing

pure confectioners' (icing)
sugar, to serve

SWEET PASTRY

1¼ cups (190 g) gluten-free
all-purpose (plain) flour

¼ cup (30 g) confectioners'
(icing) sugar

2¾ oz (80 g) butter or
dairy-free margarine

1 egg, lightly beaten, or
equivalent egg substitute,
approximately

BUTTERNUT AND
COCONUT FILLING

1½ cups (375 g) cooked
mashed butternut squash
(pumpkin)

3 eggs, or equivalent
egg substitute, lightly beaten

¾ cup (185 g) soft brown sugar

½ cup (125 g) sour cream

1 oz (30 g) fresh coconut,
grated

3 tablespoons golden syrup

Prep time: 25 minutes
Cooking time: 1¼ hours
Serves 8–10

Preheat the oven to 400°F (200°C/Gas 6). Lightly grease a 9 in (23 cm) loose-based flan tin with butter.

For the pastry, sift the flour and confectioners' sugar into a large bowl. Rub the butter into the flour with your fingertips until the mixture resembles dry breadcrumbs. Make a well in the center and add enough egg to form a dough. Turn the dough onto a lightly floured board and knead lightly until no longer sticky.

Roll out between two sheets of lightly floured baking paper until large enough to line the prepared tin. Reserve any leftover dough.

Place the tin on a baking tray. Cover the pastry with a sheet of crumpled baking paper and fill with baking beads or rice. Bake for 10 minutes. Remove the beads and paper and bake for a further 10–15 minutes, or until lightly browned. Fill any cracks with small amounts of reserved pastry. Bake for a further 2 minutes to set. Remove from the oven and cool completely. Reduce the oven temperature to 350°F (180°C/Gas 4).

For the butternut and coconut filling, combine all the ingredients in a large bowl and mix together well. Place the cooled pastry case on a baking tray and pour in the filling.

Bake for 45 minutes, or until the filling is just set. Cool completely before serving. Dust the edges lightly with confectioners' sugar.

HINT: Packaged shredded coconut contains preservatives. Buy a fresh coconut and grate it yourself. Alternatively, omit the coconut.

mini pear meringue tarts

Low chemical.
Contains egg. Free of dairy, gluten, nut and soy.

1 quantity Sweet pastry (see the recipe on the opposite page), uncooked

2 canned pear halves, puréed

1½ tablespoons sugar

¼ teaspoon citric acid

1 tablespoon maize cornstarch (cornflour)

¼ cup (60 ml) Pear Juice (see Basics)

MERINGUE

1 egg white

2 tablespoons sugar

Prep time: 25 minutes
Cooking time: 20 minutes
Makes 12 small tarts

Preheat the oven to 425°F (220°C/Gas 7). Lightly grease twelve small tart cases, cupcake tins or ⅓ cup (80 ml) muffin holes. Cut the dough into 12 portions. Roll out each portion until it is large enough to fit into the tart cases. Press into place, then prick the bases lightly all over with a fork. Bake for 10–15 minutes, or until the pastry is lightly browned.

Combine the pear purée, sugar and citric acid in a small saucepan. Blend the cornstarch and pear juice together in a small bowl and add to the pan. Stir over medium heat until the mixture boils and thickens; cool. Spoon the mixture into the pastry cases and place on a baking tray.

For the meringue, beat the egg white in a small bowl with electric beaters until stiff peaks form. Gradually add the sugar, beating well after each addition until thick and glossy.

Spread the meringue over the pear filling. Bake the tarts for 2–3 minutes, or until the meringue is golden brown.

sponge cake

Low chemical.
Contains egg. Free of dairy, gluten, nut and soy.

dairy-free margarine, for greasing

soy-free, gluten-free all-purpose (plain) flour, for dusting

4 eggs

¾ cup (165 g) sugar

1 cup (150 g) soy-free, gluten-free all-purpose (plain) flour

⅓ cup (80 ml) hot water

⅓ cup (105 g) Pear Jam (see Basics)

pure confectioners' (icing) sugar, to serve

MOCK WHIPPED CREAM
1 teaspoon powdered gelatine

⅓ cup (80 ml) cold water

4½ oz (125 g) dairy-free margarine

¼ cup (60 g) superfine (caster) sugar

½ teaspoon natural vanilla extract

Prep time: 20 minutes
Cooking time: 30 minutes
Serves 6

Preheat the oven to 350°F (180°C/Gas 4). Lightly grease and flour two 8 in (20 cm) round cake tins, then line the base with baking paper.

Beat the eggs and sugar in the small bowl of an electric mixer for about 6–7 minutes, or until light and fluffy. Sift the dry ingredients and very gently fold into the egg mixture alternately with the hot water. Gently spread the mixture into the prepared pans.

Bake for about 25–30 minutes, or until lightly brown and the cakes have slightly left the side of the tins. Turn onto a wire rack to cool.

For the mocked whipped cream, sprinkle the gelatine over the cold water in a small heatproof bowl. Stand the bowl in a small saucepan of simmering water and stir until the gelatine has dissolved. Cool slightly.

Beat the margarine, sugar and vanilla in a small bowl with electric beaters until pale in color. Gradually add the cooled gelatine mixture and beat until light and fluffy.

Spread the jam over the top of one sponge, and top with the cream. Place the other sponge on top and dust with confectioners' sugar.

HINT: This sponge has no wheat flour and no chemical raising agent, but relies on air for its lightness. Take great care when folding in dry ingredients. Use a large metal slotted spoon to ensure light, even folding.

gluten-free scones

Low chemical.
Free of egg, dairy, gluten, nut and soy.

3½ cups (525 g) soy-free, gluten-free self-raising flour

3 teaspoons gluten-free baking powder

ground sea salt

2¾ oz (80 g) dairy-free margarine

1 tablespoon superfine (caster) sugar

1¼ cups (325 ml) rice milk

Prep time: 10 minutes
Cooking time: 15 minutes
Makes 12 scones

Preheat the oven to 425°F (220°C/Gas 7). Line a baking tray with a sheet of baking paper.

Sift the flour, baking powder and a pinch of salt into a large bowl. Use your fingertips to rub the margarine into the flour until it resembles fine breadcrumbs. Stir in the sugar. Add the rice milk and use a round-bladed knife to mix until the dough just comes together.

Turn out onto a lightly floured surface and knead until combined. Press or roll out until the dough is about ¾ in (2 cm) thick. Use a 2¼ in (5.5 cm) round cutter to cut out the dough. Place on the lined tray about ½ in (1 cm) apart. Re-roll any remaining dough.

Bake for 12–15 minutes, or until cooked. Serve warm.

gluten-free herb scones

Low chemical.
Free of egg, dairy, gluten, nut and soy.

Add 2 tablespoons finely chopped fresh chives with the sugar.

gluten-free butternut scones

Moderate chemical.
Free of egg, dairy, gluten, nut and soy.

Add 1 cup (250 g) mashed and cooled butternut squash (pumpkin) with the sugar. Reduce the rice milk to ½ cup (125 ml).

traditional scones

Low chemical.
Contains dairy and gluten. Free of egg, nut and soy.

3 cups (450 g) self-raising flour

ground sea salt

2¾ oz (80 g) butter, chilled and cubed

1 tablespoon superfine (caster) sugar

1 cup (250 ml) milk

Prep time: 10 minutes
Cooking time: 15 minutes
Makes 12 scones

Preheat the oven to 425°F (220°C/Gas 7). Line a baking tray with a sheet of baking paper.

Sift the flour and salt into a large bowl. Use your fingertips to rub the butter into the flour until the mixture resembles fine breadcrumbs. Stir in the sugar. Add the milk and use a round-bladed knife to mix until the dough just comes together.

Turn out onto a lightly floured surface and knead until combined. Press or roll out until the dough is about ¾ in (2 cm) thick. Use a 2¼ in (5.5 cm) round cutter to cut out the dough. Place on the lined tray about ½ in (1 cm) apart. Re-roll any remaining dough.

Bake the scones for 12–15 minutes, or until cooked. Serve warm.

whole wheat scones

Low chemical.
Contains dairy and gluten. Free of egg, nut and soy.

For whole wheat scones, replace the self-raising flour with 3 cups (450 g) whole wheat self-raising flour.

scallion and cheese scones

Moderate chemical.
Contains dairy and gluten. Free of egg, nut and soy.

Add ¼ cup (30 g) chopped scallion (spring onion) and ½ cup (60 g) grated mild cheese with the sugar in step 2. Sprinkle a little extra cheese over the scones before baking.

gluten-free carob roll

Low chemical.
Contains egg. Free of dairy, gluten, nut and soy.

dairy-free margarine,
for greasing

3 eggs

½ cup (125 g) sugar

1 tablespoon golden syrup

½ cup (75 g) soy-free,
gluten-free self-raising flour

1 tablespoon carob powder

1 teaspoon gluten-free
baking powder

pure confectioners'
(icing) sugar

CAROB CREAM

3 oz (85 g) dairy-free
margarine

¼ cup (55 g) sugar

1½ tablespoons carob powder

2 tablespoons warm water

Prep time: 30 minutes

Cooking time: 12 minutes

Serves 4–6

Preheat the oven to 400°F (200°C/Gas 6). Lightly grease a 12 × 10 in (30 × 25 cm) jelly-roll tin and cover the base and two opposite sides with a sheet of baking paper.

Beat the eggs, sugar and golden syrup in an electric mixer for 6 minutes, or until light and fluffy. Sift together the flour, carob and baking powder and gently fold into the egg mixture. Pour the mixture into the prepared tin and spread evenly.

Bake the roll for about 10–12 minutes, or until the mixture springs back when touched with fingertips. Do not overcook. Run a knife around the edge of the tin and invert onto a large sheet of baking paper liberally dusted with sifted confectioners' sugar—carefully remove the lining paper. Roll up from the short end, enclosing the baking paper. Place on a wire rack to cool.

For the carob cream, beat the margarine, sugar and carob together until light and fluffy. Add the water and beat for 1 minute until fluffy.

Carefully unroll the roll and spread with the carob cream. Re-roll using the paper as a guide and place seam side down on a serving plate. Dust with extra confectioners' sugar if desired.

golden carob roll

Low chemical.
Contains egg, dairy and gluten. Free of nut and soy.

If gluten and dairy are part of your diet, replace the gluten-free flour with ½ cup (60 g) self-raising flour. To make the carob cream, use 3 oz (85 g) butter, ¼ cup (55 g) sugar, 2 tablespoons warm water and 1½ tablespoons carob powder and follow the same method as above.

oat cookies

Low chemical.
Contains gluten. Free of egg, dairy, nut and soy.

½ cup (75 g) soy-free, gluten-free all-purpose (plain) flour

¼ teaspoon baking soda (bicarbonate of soda)

2 tablespoons superfine (caster) sugar

1½ cups (225 g) oat bran

4½ oz (125 g) dairy-free margarine, melted and cooled

1 egg, or equivalent egg substitute

Prep time: 15 minutes
Cooking time: 15 minutes
Makes 20 cookies

Preheat the oven to 325°F (170°C/Gas 3). Line two baking trays with sheets of baking paper.

Sift the flour, baking soda and sugar into a bowl. Stir in the oat bran. Add the combined margarine and egg. Mix until well combined and the mixture forms a soft dough.

Turn the dough out onto a lightly floured surface. Use a lightly floured rolling pin to roll out the dough until ¼ in (5 mm) thick. Use a 2½ in (6 cm) round cutter to cut out the cookies. Use a spatula to carefully transfer the cookies to the lined trays.

Bake for 10–12 minutes, swapping the trays around once, or until light golden brown and cooked. Set aside on trays to cool.

HINT: These cookies are delicious served with cheese. Choose a mild cheese to keep the chemical level down.

buttery oat cookies

Low chemical.
Contains egg, dairy and gluten. Free of nut and soy.

For a more traditional cookie, replace the gluten-free flour with ½ cup (75 g) all-purpose (plain) flour. Replace the dairy-free margarine with butter and use 1 egg rather than egg substitute.

potato torte

Low chemical.
Contains egg and dairy. Free of gluten, nut and soy.

10½ oz (300 g) white-skinned potatoes, peeled and roughly chopped

canola oil, for greasing

1 tablespoon rice flour

¼ teaspoon citric acid

1 tablespoon Pear Juice (see Basics)

4 eggs, separated

⅔ cup (140 g) sugar

pure confectioners' (icing) sugar

MAPLE CREAM

1 cup (250 ml) cream

2 tablespoons maple syrup

Prep time: 35 minutes
Cooking time: 50 minutes
Serves 4–6

Boil or steam the potatoes for 15 minutes, or until tender. Drain well and mash the potatoes until smooth. You will need ¾ cup (170 g) of mashed potato for this recipe.

Preheat the oven to 350°F (180°C/Gas 4). Lightly grease a 7 in (18 cm) round cake tin, line with baking paper and grease again.

Blend the potatoes, rice flour, citric acid, pear juice and well-beaten egg yolks in a bowl until well combined. In a separate bowl, beat the egg whites to soft peaks, gradually adding the sugar. Continue beating until the whites are stiff and the sugar is dissolved.

Fold the egg white mixture into the potato mixture. Pour into the prepared tin. Bake for 30–35 minutes. Turn onto a wire rack to cool.

For the maple cream, lightly whip the cream until soft peaks form, then gently fold in the maple syrup. Chill for 10 minutes in the refrigerator before serving.

Dust the torte with confectioners' sugar and serve with maple cream.

HINT: This torte freezes well and, because of its light texture, thaws out very quickly. It can be made the day before serving. Keep refrigerated.

banana loaf

Moderate chemical.
Free of egg, dairy, gluten, nut and soy.

dairy-free margarine,
for greasing

2 cups (300 g) soy-free,
gluten-free self-raising flour

2 teaspoons gluten-free
baking powder

⅔ cup (125 g) soft brown sugar

¼ teaspoon ground cinnamon

4½ oz (125 g) dairy-free
margarine, melted and
cooled slightly

½ cup (125 ml) rice milk

2 eggs, or equivalent
egg substitute

3 large (1 lb 9 oz/700 g) ripe
bananas, mashed

golden or pure maple syrup,
to serve (optional)

Prep time: 20 minutes
Cooking time: 50 minutes
Serves 8

Preheat the oven to 325°F (170°C/Gas 3). Grease a 4½ × 8½ in (11 × 21 cm) loaf tin. Line the base of the tin with baking paper.

Sift the flour, baking powder, sugar and cinnamon into a large bowl. In a separate bowl, whisk the margarine, rice milk and egg substitute together. Add the milk mixture to the dry ingredients with the mashed bananas. Use a wooden spoon to mix until well combined.

Pour the mixture into the prepared tin and smooth the surface with a spoon. Bake for 40 minutes, or until a skewer inserted into the center comes out clean. Set aside in the tin for 5 minutes before turning out onto a wire rack to cool. Serve warm or at room temperature. Cut into slices. If desired, drizzle with a little golden or maple syrup.

HINTS: If you can tolerate dairy, spread the slices with a little low-fat ricotta cheese before drizzling with syrup.

This loaf is best eaten on the day it is made.

traditional banana loaf

Moderate chemical.
Contains egg, dairy and gluten. Free of nut and soy.

Replace the gluten-free flour with 2 cups (300 g) self-raising flour and omit the baking powder. Replace the dairy-free margarine with butter, the egg substitute with 2 eggs and the rice milk with cow's milk. Bake for 50 minutes, or until a skewer inserted into the center comes out clean. Keep in an airtight container for up to 5 days.

gluten-free pear muffins

Low chemical.
Free of egg, dairy, gluten, nut and soy.

canola oil, for greasing

2 cups (300 g) soy-free, gluten-free self-raising flour

2 teaspoons gluten-free baking powder

¾ cup lightly packed (140 g) soft brown sugar

⅔ cup (160 ml) rice milk

⅓ cup (80 ml) canola oil

2 eggs, or equivalent egg substitute

2 (1 lb/450 g) ripe pears, peeled, cored and mashed

Prep time: 15 minutes
Cooking time: 20 minutes
Makes 12 muffins

Preheat the oven to 350°F (180°C/Gas 4). Lightly grease a 12-cup ⅓ cup (80 ml) muffin tin with canola oil.

Sift the flour and baking powder into a large bowl and add the sugar. In a separate bowl, combine the rice milk, oil and egg. Add the rice milk mixture and pears to the flour mixture. Use a large metal spoon to mix until just combined. Spoon the mixture into the muffin holes.

Bake for 18–20 minutes, or until a skewer inserted in the center comes out clean. Leave for 5 minutes before turning onto a wire rack.

HINT: These muffins need to be eaten the day they are made.

gluten-free banana muffins

Moderate chemical.
Free of egg, dairy, gluten, nut and soy.

Replace the pears with 2 large ripe bananas that have been mashed.

gluten-free rhubarb muffins

Moderate chemical.
Free of egg, dairy, gluten, nut and soy.

Replace the pears with ½ bunch (7 oz/200 g) rhubarb, washed and cut into ¾ in (2 cm) pieces. Increase the rice milk to ¾ cup (185 ml).

pear muffins

Low chemical.
Contains egg, dairy and gluten. Free of nut and soy.

canola oil, for greasing

2 cups (300 g) self-raising flour

¾ cup lightly packed (140 g) soft brown sugar

⅔ cup (160 ml) milk

⅓ cup (80 ml) canola oil

2 eggs, whisked

2 (1 lb/450 g) ripe pears, peeled, cored and mashed

Prep time: 10 minutes
Cooking time: 18–20 minutes
Makes 12 muffins

Preheat the oven to 350°F (180°C/Gas 4). Lightly grease a 12-cup ⅓ cup (80 ml) muffin tin.

Sift the flour and sugar into a large bowl. In a separate bowl, combine the milk, oil and eggs. Add the milk mixture and pears to the flour mixture. Use a large metal spoon to mix until just combined. Spoon evenly among the muffin holes.

Bake for 18–20 minutes, or until a skewer inserted in the center comes out clean. Leave for 5 minutes before turning onto a wire rack.

apple and cinnamon muffins

Moderate chemical.
Contains egg, dairy and gluten. Free of nut and soy.

Add ¼ teaspoon ground cinnamon with the flour and sugar. Replace the pears with 2 apples, peeled and grated.

banana muffins

Moderate chemical.
Contains egg, dairy and gluten. Free of nut and soy.

Reduce the milk to ½ cup (125 ml) milk. Replace the pears with 2 large ripe bananas that have been mashed.

cashew cookies

Low chemical.
Contains nuts. Free of egg, dairy, gluten and soy.

1 cup (135 g) brown rice flour

½ teaspoon baking soda
(bicarbonate of soda)

¼ cup (55 g) soft brown sugar

½ cup (60 g) ground
raw cashews

¼ cup (60 ml) water

½ teaspoon natural
vanilla extract

Prep time: 10 minutes
Cooking time: 15 minutes
Makes 15 cookies

Preheat the oven to 350°F (180°C/Gas 4). Line two baking trays with sheets of baking paper.

Sift the rice flour and baking soda into a bowl. Add the sugar and cashews. Stir well to combine ingredients.

Make a well in the center, then add the water and vanilla extract. Stir and mix to a firm dough.

Roll into walnut-sized balls using rice-floured hands. Place on the prepared trays. Flatten each cookie with the back of a spoon. Bake for about 10–12 minutes, until lightly browned.

HINT: These cookies soften on storage so they are best eaten on the same day that they are baked.

One in four children with a peanut allergy will also have an allergy to another type of nut. Children who are allergic to peanuts should be screened for allergy to other nuts as well, as they are the most highly allergenic foods.

Gooey butterscotch pudding? Pavlova? Go on, indulge yourself! Your sweet tooth will never feel deprived when you discover the sweet treats in store in this chapter. Make simple family favorites, such as steamed pudding and ice cream, or create a sophisticated dessert or sweet morsel for your guests. There's even a couple of wickedly sweet adults-only indulgences.

after dinner

butterscotch pudding

Low chemical.
Free of egg, dairy, gluten, nut and soy.

dairy-free margarine,
for greasing

1¼ cups (190 g) soy-free,
gluten-free self-raising flour

1 teaspoon gluten-free
baking powder

⅓ cup firmly packed (80 g)
soft brown sugar

⅔ cup (160 ml) rice milk

2¼ oz (60 g) dairy-free
margarine, melted, cooled

1 egg, or equivalent
egg substitute

1 tablespoon golden syrup

⅔ cup firmly packed (160 g)
soft brown sugar, extra

2 tablespoons golden
syrup, extra

1⅔ cups (410 ml)
boiling water

Prep time: 20 minutes
Cooking time: 45 minutes
Serves 4–6

Preheat the oven to 325°F (170°C/Gas 3). Lightly grease a 1.25 liter (5 cup) ovenproof dish with margarine.

Sift the flour and baking powder into a large bowl. Add the sugar. In a separate bowl, whisk the rice milk, margarine, egg and golden syrup together. Pour into the flour mixture and whisk until a smooth batter forms. Pour into the prepared dish. Place the dish on a baking tray.

Sprinkle the extra brown sugar over the batter. Combine the extra golden syrup and the boiling water and carefully pour over the batter. Bake the pudding for 35–45 minutes, or until a skewer inserted halfway into the pudding comes out clean.

Set the pudding aside for 5–10 minutes to allow the sauce to thicken slightly before serving.

traditional butterscotch pudding

Low chemical.
Contains egg, dairy and gluten. Free of nut and soy.

Replace the gluten-free self-raising flour with 1 cup (150 g) self-raising flour. Omit the baking powder. Replace the rice milk with ½ cup (125 ml) cow's milk. Replace the margarine with butter. Use 1 egg instead of egg substitute. Reduce the extra brown sugar to ½ cup (115 g). Reduce the boiling water to 1¼ cups (325 ml).

carob self-saucing pudding

Low chemical.
Contains soy. Free of egg, dairy, gluten and nut.

dairy-free margarine,
for greasing

1¼ cups (190 g) soy-containing,
gluten-free self-raising flour

1 teaspoon gluten-free
baking powder

⅓ cup firmly packed (80 g)
soft brown sugar

⅔ cup (160 ml) rice
milk, warmed

2 tablespoons carob powder

2¼ oz (60 g) dairy-free
margarine, melted, cooled

1 egg, or equivalent
egg substitute

⅔ cup firmly packed (160 g)
brown sugar, extra

1½ cups (375 ml)
boiling water

2 tablespoons carob
powder, extra

Prep time: 20 minutes
Cooking time: 45 minutes
Serves 4–6

Preheat the oven to 325°F (170°C/Gas 3). Lightly grease a 1.25 liter (5 cup) capacity ovenproof dish with margarine.

Sift the flour and baking powder into a large bowl. Add the sugar. In a separate bowl, whisk the rice milk and carob powder together until smooth. Set aside to cool. Whisk in the margarine and egg, pour into the flour mixture and whisk until a smooth batter forms. Pour into the prepared dish. Place the dish on a baking tray.

Sprinkle the extra brown sugar over the batter. Whisk the boiling water and extra carob powder together until smooth. Carefully pour over the batter. Bake for 35–45 minutes, or until a skewer inserted halfway into the pudding comes out clean. Serve immediately.

HINT: This recipe requires soy-containing gluten-free flour in order to work properly. Soy-containing flour behaves more like gluten flour.

traditional carob pudding

Low chemical.
Contains egg, dairy and gluten. Free of nut and soy.

Replace the gluten-free self-raising flour with 1 cup (150 g) self-raising flour. Omit the baking powder. Replace the rice milk with ½ cup (125 ml) cow's milk. Replace the dairy-free margarine with butter. Use 1 egg instead of the egg substitute.

maple syrup mousse

Low chemical.
Contains egg, dairy and alcohol. Free of gluten, nut and soy.

1 tablespoon powdered gelatine

2 tablespoons cold water

½ cup (125 ml) pure maple syrup

3 egg yolks

2 cups (500 ml) softly whipped cream

2 tablespoons whisky

whipped cream, extra, for decorating

Prep time: 20 minutes
Cooking time: 10 minutes
Serves 4–6

Sprinkle the gelatine over the cold water in a small heatproof bowl. Stand the bowl in a small saucepan of simmering water and stir until the gelatine has dissolved. Cool slightly.

In a small saucepan, heat the maple syrup over medium heat, then add the dissolved gelatine. In the small bowl of an electric mixer, beat the egg yolks until thick and light. Add a little of the hot syrup mixture to the egg mixture. Gradually add the rest of the syrup mixture, stirring until they are completely combined.

Cool the mixture in the refrigerator until it is the consistency of unbeaten egg white.

Gently fold the cream and whisky into the maple mixture. Scoop into a large serving dish. Chill until set. Decorate with extra whipped cream.

HINT: For a lighter textured mousse, beat 3 egg whites to a soft foam. Fold carefully through the completed mixture.

hazelnut and maple syrup mousse

Moderate chemical.
Contains nuts, egg, dairy and alcohol. Free of gluten and soy.

If nuts are permissible in your diet and you can tolerate extra salicylates and amines, add interest to the flavor and texture of the mousse by folding ¼ cup (30 g) roughly chopped hazelnuts into the lightly whipped cream and using 10 whole hazelnuts as decoration.

coffee-baked pears

Low chemical.
Contains alcohol. Free of egg, dairy, gluten, nut and soy.

4 large (3 lb/1.3 kg) pears

1 oz (25 g) butter or
dairy-free margarine, melted

⅓ cup firmly packed (80 g)
soft brown sugar

2 tablespoons pure
maple syrup

1 tablespoon whisky

1 tablespoon prepared strong
decaffeinated black coffee

Prep time: 15 minutes

Cooking time: 20 minutes

Serves 4

Preheat the oven to 350°F (180°C/Gas 4). Thickly peel the pears, then core them and cut in half lengthways. Put the prepared pears, cut side down, in an ovenproof dish.

Put the butter, sugar, maple syrup, whisky and black coffee in a bowl and mix together thoroughly. Spoon the mixture over the pears. Bake for 20 minutes, or until the pears are tender. Serve warm.

HINTS: Use a melon baller to remove the seeds and core from the pears. The pears are best prepared just before you are going to cook them. Otherwise, they may discolor.

If you are sensitive to chemicals, choose decaffeinated coffee instead of caffeinated coffee. It has lower levels of chemicals than caffeinated coffee and is just as good as a beverage and for using in recipes. Most coffee shops these days offer decaffeinated coffee on their menus.

coffee-baked bananas

Moderate chemical.
Contains alcohol. Free of egg, dairy, gluten, nut and soy.

If you feel like a change, use 4 just-ripe bananas instead of the pears. Peel them, then slice them in half along their length.

cashew ice cream

Low chemical.
Contains nuts. Free of egg, dairy, gluten and soy.

2 teaspoons powdered gelatine

2 tablespoons cold water

3 cups (750 ml) cashew nut milk

¼ cup (30 g) pure confectioners' (icing) sugar

¼ cup (60 ml) canola oil

1 teaspoon natural vanilla extract

3 x 15 oz (425 g) can pears in syrup, drained and puréed

Prep time: 25 minutes + overnight freezing

Cooking time: 5 minutes

Serves 4–6

Sprinkle the gelatine over 2 tablespoons cold water in a small heatproof bowl. Stand the bowl in a small saucepan of simmering water and stir until the gelatine has dissolved. Cool.

Meanwhile, blend the nut milk, sugar, oil and vanilla. Blend or stir in the pears and add the cooled gelatine.

Pour the mixture into a metal dish and place in the freezer. Freeze until large ice crystals form. Remove the mixture from the freezer. Beat for 2–3 minutes. Return to the freezer and freeze until almost completely frozen. Remove and beat again.

Return to the freezer and freeze until completely frozen. Ice cream is best eaten within 3–4 days.

HINT: If you can't find ready-made nut milk, you can make your own by processing nuts until they form a paste and adding enough water to form a creamy consistency. Nut paste can also be bought at many health food stores. Process further, adding enough water to form a creamy consistency.

tropical ice cream

Moderate chemical.
Contains nuts. Free of egg, dairy, gluten and soy.

Try making a different flavored ice cream. Try either 3 cups (550 g) chopped mango or cherimoya (custard apple) instead of the pears.

gluten-free steamed pudding

Low chemical.
Free of egg, dairy, gluten, nut and soy.

dairy-free margarine, for greasing

½ cup (175 g) golden syrup or Pear Jam (see Basics)

4½ oz (125 g) dairy-free margarine, extra

½ cup (115 g) superfine (caster) sugar

2 eggs, lightly beaten, or equivalent egg substitute

1½ cups (225 g) soy-free, gluten-free all-purpose (plain) flour

1½ teaspoons gluten-free baking powder

⅓ cup (80 ml) water

heavy (thick/double) cream, for serving (optional)

Prep time: 40 minutes
Cooking time: 35 minutes
Makes 6 puddings

Preheat the oven to 350°F (180°C/Gas 4). Lightly grease six ⅔ cup (160 ml) molds with margarine, then line the bases with rounds of baking paper. Grease six squares of aluminium foil, larger than the tops of the molds and make a pleat in each one. Put a tablespoon of golden syrup or pear jam in the base of each mold.

In the large bowl of an electric mixer, beat the margarine and sugar until light and fluffy. Add the eggs, one at a time, beating well after each addition. Add the sifted flour and baking powder alternately with the water. Mix gently until well combined.

Divide the batter evenly among the prepared molds. Cover with the pleated, greased aluminium foil. Sit the molds in a baking dish and pour in enough boiling water to come halfway up the sides of the molds. Bake for about 30 minutes, or until a skewer inserted into the center of the pudding comes out clean. Invert onto serving plates and serve with dollops of heavy cream, if desired.

HINT: Steamed puddings are best made close to serving.

steamed jam pudding

Low chemical.
Contains gluten. Free of egg, dairy, nut and soy.

If you can consume gluten without problems, replace the gluten-free flour with 1½ cups (225 g) self-raising flour, omit the baking powder and reduce the water to ¼ cup (60 ml).

pear sorbet

Low chemical.
Free of egg, dairy, gluten, nut and soy.

6 large (4 lb 8 oz/2 kg)
very ripe pears
2 cups (440 g) sugar
7 fl oz (200 ml) water

Prep time: 40 minutes +
overnight freezing
Cooking time: 15 minutes
Serves 4–6

Thickly peel the pears, then core them and slice them into thick pieces. Place the pears in a large saucepan, just cover with water and simmer for about 10 minutes, or until tender. Drain and allow to cool.

Purée the pears in a blender or food processor until smooth.

Combine the sugar and water in a saucepan over medium heat and stir until the sugar has dissolved. Allow the syrup to cool. Mix together the sugar syrup and pear purée, then pour into a shallow metal pan. Freeze until just solid.

Remove the pan from the freezer. Beat or process until a 'slush' forms. Return to the pan and freeze until firm.

HINT: Sorbets may be served before the main course to refresh the palate, or with other creams or fruit as a dessert.

tamarillo sorbet

Moderate chemical.
Free of egg, dairy, gluten, nut and soy.

Tamarillo is a plum-red fruit the size of an egg, containing moderate levels of salicylates. The seeds are soft and can be eaten or, if you prefer when using for sorbet, strain the purée to remove the seeds. Make tamarillo sorbet by plunging 4 large (1 lb/450 g) tamarillos into boiling water for 15 seconds, then into cold water. Remove the skins, which will slip off easily. Purée the fruit by either blending or pushing through a sieve. Use tamarillo purée in place of half the pears.

frozen yogurt

Low chemical.
Contains dairy. Free of egg, gluten, nut and soy.

2⅓ cups (600 g)
full-cream natural yogurt

½ cup (110 g) sugar

1 teaspoon natural
vanilla extract

Prep time: 15 minutes +
overnight freezing
Cooking time: Nil
Serves 4–6

Beat the yogurt with the sugar and vanilla. Pour the mixture into a shallow metal pan, cover with foil and place in the freezer.

When half-frozen, remove from the freezer and blend in a blender or food processor until smooth. Return to the freezer until solid. Store in a sealed container to prevent freezer burn.

Allow the frozen yogurt to soften for 15–20 minutes in the refrigerator before serving.

HINT: Use plain homemade or store bought yogurt for this recipe. If skim milk yogurt is used, it will result in a coarse grainy-textured ice, so it is best to use full-cream yogurt.

tropical frozen yogurt

Moderate chemical.
Contains dairy. Free of egg, gluten, nut and soy.

The plain frozen yogurt can be used as a base for a tropical frozen yogurt dessert. Fold 2 small finely chopped mangoes, 2 finely chopped tamarillos, 8 finely chopped loquats and 1 cup (250 ml) softly whipped cream into the yogurt after blending. Return to the freezer until solid.

pears with sabayon sauce

Low chemical.
Contains egg. Free of dairy, gluten, nut and soy.

6 small (2 lb 4 oz/1 kg)
firm pears, with stems
attached
½ cup (110 g) sugar
1½ cups (375 ml) water
1 teaspoon citric acid

SABAYON SAUCE
3 egg yolks
1 tablespoon sugar
2 tablespoons Pear Juice
(see Basics)
½ teaspoon citric acid

Prep time: 25 minutes
Cooking time: 25 minutes
Serves 4–6

Thickly peel the pears, leaving them whole with the stems intact.

Combine the sugar and water in a saucepan over medium heat and stir until the sugar has dissolved. Reduce the heat to low and add the citric acid. Stir to combine. Gently lower the peeled pears into the syrup and cover with a lid. Poach gently for 10–15 minutes, or until tender but still firm. Remove the pears from the syrup. Increase the heat to medium and bring the syrup to a rapid simmer. Cook until the syrup reaches a coating consistency. Pour the syrup over the pears.

For the sabayon sauce, put all the ingredients in a small heatproof bowl and sit over a saucepan of simmering water. Whisk the sauce until it becomes very frothy and starts to thicken. Serve at once with the poached pears.

HINT: To prevent the pears from discoloring, dissolve 2 teaspoons citric acid in 1 liter (4 cups) of water. Keep the pears immersed until all are prepared for poaching. Rinse in cold water before cooking.

tamarillos with gin sabayon sauce

Moderate chemical.
Contains egg and alcohol. Free of dairy, gluten, nut and soy.

For an exotic desert, use tamarillos in place of the pears. Plunge 6 (about 1 lb 9 oz/700 g) tamarillos into a saucepan of boiling water for 1 minute. Remove from the pan and plunge into cold water. Slip off the skins. Omit the citric acid from the poaching liquid and instead add 1 tablespoon gin. Poach the tamarillos in the same way as the pears. Add 1 tablespoon gin to the Sabayon sauce. Cut the tamarillos into four, leaving the end near the stem intact.

angel pear flan

Low chemical.
Contains egg. Free of dairy, gluten, nut and soy.

canola oil, for greasing

maize cornstarch (cornflour),
for dusting

MERINGUE CRUST

2 egg whites

pinch of ground sea salt

pinch of cream of tartar

½ cup (115 g) superfine
(caster) sugar

PEAR FILLING

2 tablespoons maize
cornstarch (cornflour)

2 tablespoons sugar

2 x 15 oz (425 g) cans pears
in syrup, drained and puréed

2 egg yolks

1 teaspoon citric acid

TOPPING AND GLAZE

3 canned pear halves,
thinly sliced

1 cup (250 ml) Pear Juice
(see Basics)

3 teaspoons arrowroot

Prep time: 50 minutes

Cooking time: 1¼ hours

Serves 4–6

Preheat the oven to 275°F (140°C/Gas 1). Lightly grease an 8 in (20 cm) pie plate or flan tin and dust with maize cornstarch.

For the meringue crust, beat the egg whites with the salt and cream of tartar until stiff, white and dry. Add the sugar gradually, beating well after each addition. Spread the meringue across the bottom and up the sides of the prepared pie plate. Bake for 1 hour. Allow the meringue to cool completely.

Meanwhile, prepare the filling. In a saucepan, blend the cornstarch and sugar with the pear purée, egg yolks and citric acid. Cook over medium heat until the mixture boils and thickens, stirring constantly. Allow to cool. Scoop the cooled filling into the cooled meringue base. Chill in the refrigerator until set.

For the topping and glaze, arrange well-drained pear slices on the filling. Blend the pear juice with the arrowroot in a small saucepan and cook over medium heat until the mixture boils and thickens. Cool slightly. Pour over the pear slices. Chill in the refrigerator until cold.

HINT: This is best eaten on the day it is made, although you can make the base the day before and store it in an airtight container.

pear mallow dessert

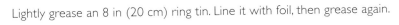

Low chemical.
Contains egg and gluten. Free of dairy, nut and soy.

canola oil, for greasing

2 x 7 in (18 cm) day-old sponge cake layers

1 lb 13 oz (825 g) can pear halves, each one cut into 4 pieces

1½ cups (375 ml) boiling water

2 teaspoons powdered gelatine

2 cups (440 g) sugar

Prep time: 45 minutes + overnight setting
Cooking time: 25 minutes
Serves 4–6

Lightly grease an 8 in (20 cm) ring tin. Line it with foil, then grease again.

Break the sponge into 1½ in (3.5 cm) pieces. Place one-third of the pieces in the base of the prepared ring tin. Set the rest aside. Top with half the pear pieces and reserve the rest.

In a small saucepan, pour half the water over the gelatine and stir until dissolved. Bring the mixture back to a boil and boil for 10–12 minutes. Add the rest of the water and mix in the sugar. Heat gently, stirring, over medium heat. Bring to a boil again and boil without stirring for 12 minutes. Remove from the heat and cool slightly. Pour the mixture into the large bowl of an electric mixer. Beat until the mixture doubles in bulk and becomes thick and white.

Spoon half the marshmallow mixture on top of the sponge and pear layer. Top with half of the remaining sponge and all the reserved pear pieces. Spoon over the rest of the marshmallow mixture. Lastly, top with the remaining sponge. Press down gently but firmly with your hand. Refrigerate for 2–3 hours (preferably overnight), or until the marshmallow has set. Upturn on to a serving platter.

HINT: This dessert keeps well for 2–3 days in the refrigerator.

carob mallow dessert

Low chemical.
Contains egg, dairy, gluten and soy. Free of nut.

Chop 1¼ cups (200 g) carob chips and place in a heatproof bowl with 2 tablespoons dairy-free margarine. Melt over a pan of simmering water, without letting the bowl touch the water. Add the carob filling on top of the pear layers, then continue with the recipe.

crepes with two sauces

Low chemical.
Free of egg, dairy, gluten, nut and soy.

MOCHA TOFFEE SAUCE

1 tablespoon golden syrup

1½ teaspoons instant
decaffeinated coffee powder

1 tablespoon maize
cornstarch (cornflour)

½ cup firmly packed (115 g)
soft brown sugar

1 cup (250 ml) water

TANGY PEAR SAUCE

1 cup (250 ml) Pear Juice
(see Basics)

2 tablespoons superfine
(caster) sugar

1 tablespoon maize
cornstarch (cornflour)

¼ teaspoon citric acid

CREPES

1¼ cups (190 g) soy-free,
gluten-free all-purpose
(plain) flour

2 teaspoons gluten-free
baking powder

1 egg, or equivalent egg
substitute

2 tablespoons canola oil

1¼ cups (310 ml) water

Prep time: 35 minutes
Cooking time: 25 minutes
Makes 10 crepes

For the mocha toffee sauce, combine the syrup, coffee powder, cornstarch and sugar in a wide pan. Add the water and blend. Put the pan over medium heat. Stir constantly until the mixture boils and thickens. Reduce the heat and simmer for 2–3 minutes. Set aside.

For the tangy pear sauce, combine the pear juice and sugar in a small saucepan. Blend the cornstarch with a little of the pear juice and add to the pan. Cook, stirring over medium heat, until the mixture boils and thickens. Stir in the citric acid. Set aside.

For the crepes, sift the flour and baking powder into a bowl. Gradually add the combined egg, 1 tablespoon of the oil and the water, stirring well until the batter is smooth and the consistency of thin cream, adding more water if needed. Strain into a vessel with a pouring lip.

Lightly brush an 8 in (20 cm) frying pan with a little of the remaining oil and heat over medium heat. Pour in just enough crepe batter to thinly cover the bottom of the pan. When the top of the crepe starts to set, turn it over with a spatula. After browning the second side, transfer to a plate. Repeat with the remaining crepe batter, greasing the pan between each. Fold each crepe in four to form a triangle.

Reheat the sauces in two frying pans over low heat. Put half the crepes in each pan and heat gently until warmed through. Place the crepes on two serving plates and spoon any extra warm sauce over the top.

HINT: If you can tolerate gluten and dairy, you can make the crepes from all-purpose (plain) flour and cow's milk—see the recipe on page 33.

pavlova

Moderate chemical.
Contains egg and soy. Free of dairy, gluten and nut.

4 x 2¼ oz (59 g) egg whites, at room temperature

ground sea salt

1 cup (230 g) superfine (caster) sugar

1 teaspoon natural vanilla extract

soy yogurt, to serve

1 mango, sliced

1 banana, sliced

Prep time: 15 minutes + cooling time
Cooking time: 1½ hours
Serves 8

Preheat the oven to 225°F (110°C/Gas ½). Line a large baking tray with baking paper. Draw a 9 in (23 cm) circle on the paper and place the paper pencil side down on the tray.

Use an electric mixer to beat the egg whites and a pinch of salt until soft peaks form. Gradually add the sugar (about 1–2 tablespoons at a time), beating well between each addition. Stir in the vanilla.

Spoon the meringue onto the prepared tray and use a spoon to spread over the circle. Bake for 1¼–1½ hours. Turn the oven off and keep the oven door ajar. Leave the meringue to cool in the oven for 2–3 hours, or until cooled completely.

To serve, spread soy yogurt over the top of the pavlova, then top with slices of mango and banana.

pavlova with cream

Moderate chemical.
Contains egg and dairy. Free of gluten, nut and soy.

For an indulgent treat, replace the soy yogurt with whipped cream.

banana and caramel tart

Moderate chemical.
Contains egg and dairy. Free of gluten, nut and soy.

14 oz (400 g) can condensed milk

2 eggs, lightly whisked

2¼ oz (60 g) butter, melted

½ cup lightly packed (95 g) soft brown sugar

1 teaspoon natural vanilla extract

2 large (1 lb/450 g) bananas, thickly sliced

1 cooked 9 in (23 cm) gluten-free pastry shell (see the recipe on page 168)

pure confectioners' (icing) sugar, to serve

Prep time: 25 minutes, including pastry

Cooking time: 1 hour

Serves 8–10

Preheat the oven to 325°F (170°C/Gas 3). To make the filling, put the condensed milk, eggs, melted butter, brown sugar and vanilla extract in a large bowl. Whisk everything together.

Arrange the bananas over the base of the cooked pastry shell. Place the tart case on a baking tray lined with baking paper. Pour the filling over the banana and bake for 35 minutes, or until just set. Remove from the oven and set aside to cool to room temperature.

To serve, cut the tart into wedges and dust with confectioners' sugar.

mocha ricotta pie

Low chemical.
Contains nuts, dairy, soy and alcohol. Free of egg and gluten.

butter, for greasing

CASHEW NUT CRUST

6½ oz (185 g) cashews, finely
chopped or processed in
a blender

2 thick rice cakes, crushed

¼ cup (55 g) sugar

2¼ oz (60 g) butter
or dairy-free margarine

MOCHA RICOTTA CREAM

2 teaspoons instant
decaffeinated coffee powder

2 tablespoons whisky
or water

2 cups (500 g) ricotta cheese

½ cup firmly packed (115 g)
soft brown sugar

¾ cup (120 g) carob
chips, chopped

1 tablespoon carob powder

Prep time: 35 minutes
Cooking time: 15 minutes
Serves 6

Preheat the oven to 350°F (180°C/Gas 4). Lightly grease a 9 in (23 cm) flan tin or pie plate.

To make the cashew nut crust, combine the cashews, crushed rice cakes and sugar in a bowl. Rub in the butter. Press the mixture into the prepared tin. Bake for 12–15 minutes, or until pale golden brown. Allow the crust to cool completely.

To make the mocha ricotta cream, dissolve the coffee in whisky or water in a bowl. Add the ricotta and brown sugar and beat until smooth. Stir in the chopped carob chips.

Spoon the filling into the prepared crust. Dust with carob powder. Refrigerate before serving.

HINT: The base and filling can be prepared the day before. Place the filling in the base on day of serving. Chill well before serving. Ask your health food store whether their carob chips contain dairy and/or soy.

golden syrup snaps

Low chemical.
Contains dairy. Free of egg, gluten, nut and soy.

2¼ oz (60 g) butter

½ cup firmly packed (115 g) soft brown sugar

2 tablespoons golden syrup

¼ cup (45 g) rice flour

¼ cup (30 g) maize cornstarch (cornflour)

½ teaspoon baking powder

7 fl oz (200 ml) cream, whipped

Prep time: 40 minutes
Cooking time: 1½ hours
Makes 20–24 snaps

Preheat the oven to 375°F (190°C/Gas 5). Cover a baking tray with baking paper or greased greaseproof paper.

Put the butter, sugar and golden syrup in a saucepan over medium—low heat. Heat until the butter has melted, then take the pan off the heat. Sift the flour, cornstarch and baking powder into the golden syrup mixture, then stir together well.

Place teaspoons of the mixture onto the prepared baking tray—only bake two at a time because you need to work quickly once they are baked. Bake for about 8 minutes, or until firm around the edges. Cool for 2 minutes then roll each snap around the handle of a wooden spoon. Leave them to cool on a wire rack, then fill with whipped cream.

HINT: If the snaps cool too quickly, return to the oven for a minute or two to soften, then roll. Best eaten on the day they are made.

golden syrup snaps with mocha cream

Low chemical.
Contains dairy and alcohol. Free of egg, gluten, nut and soy.

For a special filling, add 1 teaspoon instant decaffeinated coffee powder, 1–2 tablespoons whisky and 2 teaspoons pure confectioners' (icing) sugar to the cream before whipping.

carob truffles

Low chemical.
Contains dairy. Free of egg, gluten, nut and soy.

1¼ cups (200 g) carob chips

2¼ oz (60 g) butter or dairy-free margarine

⅓ cup (40 g) pure confectioners' (icing) sugar, sifted

1 tablespoon whisky, or prepared strong decaffeinated coffee

Prep time: 15 minutes

Cooking time: 10 minutes

Makes 15–20 truffles

Put the carob chips in a heatproof bowl over a saucepan of simmering water. Stir once or twice until completely melted.

Put the butter and confectioners' sugar in a small bowl and beat until well mixed and creamy. Add the melted carob and whisky or coffee, beating well. Allow to firm a little in the refrigerator before handling. Roll the mixture into small balls. Place on a foil-covered tray and keep in the refrigerator until ready to serve.

HINT: Check with your health food store whether their carob chips contain soy. All carob chips contain dairy.

If you can tolerate eggs, beat in an egg yolk with the butter and sugar mixture for a richer truffle.

cream cheese truffles

Low chemical.
Contains dairy. Free of egg, gluten, nut and soy.

7 oz (200 g) cream cheese

⅓ cup (40 g) pure confectioners' (icing) sugar, sifted, plus 1 cup (120 g) extra

1 teaspoon natural vanilla extract

Prep time: 20 minutes

Cooking time: Nil

Makes 15–20 truffles

In the small bowl of an electric mixer, beat together the cream cheese, confectioners' sugar and vanilla until the mixture is light and fluffy. Place in the refrigerator to chill before handling.

Form teaspoons of the mixture into balls, then roll in the extra sifted confectioners' sugar. Keep refrigerated until serving.

golden nougat

Low chemical.
Contains egg. Free of dairy, gluten, nut and soy.

2 cups (440 g) granulated
sugar
½ cup (125 ml) water
½ cup (175 g) golden syrup
1 egg white
canola oil, for greasing

Prep time: 20 minutes
Cooking time: 20 minutes
Serves 4–6

Put the sugar, water and golden syrup in a large saucepan. Heat over medium–low heat, stirring constantly until the sugar is completely dissolved. Bring to a boil and cook without stirring for about 10 minutes, or until the temperature reaches 248°F (120°C) on a sugar thermometer, or until a blob of syrup forms a very firm but pliable ball that holds its shape at room temperature. Remove the pan from the heat immediately. Pour the caramel syrup into a heatproof vessel with a pouring lip.

Just before the syrup is ready, beat the egg white until stiff but not dry. Pour the caramel mixture in a thin, continuous stream over the egg white while beating continually, until the mixture is thick and satiny.

Divide the mixture into four and stand on a marble slab or oiled aluminium foil, to cool. Shape the mixture into rolls. Leave to stand until firm enough to slice. Pieces of nougat can be wrapped in cellophane, wax paper or rice paper, but there's no need to wrap the nougat if serving immediately.

italian nut cookies

Low chemical.
Contains nuts and egg. Free of dairy, gluten and soy.

canola oil, for greasing

maize cornstarch (cornflour),
for dusting

1 cup (125 g) coarsely
ground cashews

1 cup (220 g) sugar

2 egg whites

½ teaspoon natural
vanilla extract

Prep time: 15 minutes

Cooking time: 12–15 minutes
per tray

Makes 20 cookies

Preheat the oven to 350°F (180°C/Gas 4). Lightly grease two baking trays, then dust with maize cornstarch.

Combine the ground cashews, sugar and egg whites in the small bowl of an electric mixer. Beat on medium speed for 3 minutes. Gently stir in the vanilla. Allow the mixture to stand for 5 minutes.

Place teaspoons of the mixture on the prepared trays. Bake for 12–15 minutes. Leave on the trays for a few minutes before removing with a metal spatula. Cool on a wire rack.

HINT: These cookies store well in an airtight container.

maple-glazed nuts

Low chemical.
Contains nuts. Free of egg, dairy, gluten and soy.

canola oil, for greasing

1 cup (155 g) cashews

½ cup (125 ml) pure
maple syrup

1 tablespoon golden syrup

Prep time: 10 minutes

Cooking time: 5 minutes

Serves 4–6

Lightly oil a baking tray. Spread out the cashews in a single layer on the prepared tray.

Combine the maple syrup and golden syrup in a small saucepan. Heat until the mixture reaches 248°F (120°C) on a sugar thermometer, or until a blob of syrup forms a very firm but pliable ball that holds its shape at room temperature.

Working quickly, pour the syrup over the cashews on the tray, making sure all the nuts are coated. Allow to set. Break into pieces.

coffee slushy

Low chemical.
Free of egg, dairy, gluten, nut and soy.

27½ fl oz (800 ml) water
½ cup (110 g) sugar
5 teaspoons decaffeinated instant coffee powder

Prep time: 5 minutes + freezing
Cooking time: 5 minutes
Serves 4–6

Put the water, sugar and coffee in a saucepan over low heat. Stir until the sugar is dissolved. Remove from the heat and cool.

Pour into a shallow metal tin and freeze for about 1 hour, or until just frozen around edges. Scrape this ice back into the mixture with a fork. Repeat every 30 minutes until the mixture has even-sized ice crystals. Serve immediately or beat with a fork and refreeze until just before serving. Allow to soften slightly in the refrigerator before using. The mixture should be slushy.

Pile into tall chilled glasses to serve.

HINT: The slushy can be softened in the refrigerator or placed straight from the freezer into an electric food processor. Process on low speed for 30 seconds and serve immediately.

irish coffee slushy

Low chemical.
Contains alcohol. Free of egg, dairy, gluten, nut and soy.

Try this iced version of Irish coffee. Pour ½–1 fl oz (15–30 ml) whisky per serve over the coffee slushy.

vodka pear slushy

Low chemical.
Contains alcohol. Free of egg, dairy, gluten, nut and soy.

1 lb 13 oz (825 g) can pear
halves in syrup

1 teaspoon citric acid

vodka, to serve

Prep time: 5 minutes +
freezing
Cooking time: Nil
Serves 4–6

Put the pears, syrup and citric acid into an electric blender. Blend on high for 2–3 minutes.

Pour the mixture into a shallow metal tin and freeze for about 1 hour, or until just frozen around edges. Scrape this ice back into the mixture with a fork. Repeat every 30 minutes until the mixture has even-sized ice crystals. Serve immediately or beat with a fork and refreeze until just before serving. Allow to soften slightly in the refrigerator before using. The mixture should be slushy.

Pile into tall chilled glasses and serve with a spoon and a straw. Pour ½–1 fl oz (15–30 ml) vodka over each slushy before serving.

HINT: For a non-alcoholic version of this treat, see page 232.

Most alcoholic drinks are very high in salicylates and amines, and many also contain natural glutamates. Gin, vodka and whisky have the lowest level of food chemicals of any spirit.

Parties and special occasions can present problems for children with food intolerances. But there's no need for them to feel deprived or left out of the party fun. From sweets and drinks, to iced treats and spectacular birthday cakes, the recipes in this chapter will ensure that your child can celebrate happily within safe dietary guidelines. And little friends will find the food just as yummy too.

kids

crunchy chicken bits

Low chemical.
Free of egg, dairy, gluten, nut and soy.

canola oil, for greasing

2 lb 4 oz (1 kg) chicken thigh fillets or breast fillets

¼ cup (40 g) soy-free, gluten-free all-purpose (plain) flour

2 eggs, or equivalent egg substitute

2 tablespoons water

10½ oz (300 g) plain potato chips, crushed

Prep time: 30 minutes
Cooking time: 20 minutes
Serves 4–6

Preheat the oven to 350°F (180°C/Gas 4). Lightly grease two baking trays.

Cut the chicken into 1¼ in (3 cm) pieces. Coat the chicken lightly in the flour, then dip in the combined mixture of the egg and water. Roll in the potato chips, pressing on firmly.

Lay out the chicken in a single layer on the prepared trays and bake for about 15–20 minutes, or until cooked through and golden brown. Turn once during cooking.

HINT: For an extra crunchy chicken bit, deep-fry in hot canola oil until cooked and golden brown.

crunchy chicken bits with chives

Low chemical.
Free of egg, dairy, gluten, nut and soy.

Add ¼ cup (15 g) finely chopped fresh chives to the potato chips. Follow the same method.

crunchy chicken bits with garlic

Low chemical.
Free of egg, dairy, gluten, nut and soy.

Fry 1–2 crushed garlic cloves in a small amount of canola oil. Cool, then add to the potato chips. Follow the same method.

mini veal potato pies

Low chemical.
Free of egg, dairy, gluten, nut and soy.

canola oil, for greasing

2 lb 4 oz (1 kg) white-skinned potatoes, peeled and roughly chopped

2 teaspoons canola oil

1 tablespoon canola oil, extra

1 cup (150 g) soy-free, gluten-free self-raising flour

½ teaspoon gluten-free baking powder

½ teaspoon ground sea salt

2 eggs, or equivalent egg substitute

FILLING

2 teaspoons canola oil

1 lb 2 oz (500 g) ground (minced) veal or chicken

¾ cup (185 ml) fresh Veal or Chicken Stock (see Basics)

1½ tablespoons maize cornstarch (cornflour), blended with 1 tablespoon water

1 teaspoon ground sea salt

1 tablespoon finely chopped fresh parsley

Prep time: 35 minutes

Cooking time: 35 minutes

Makes 24 pies

Preheat the oven to 350°F (180°C/Gas 4). Lightly grease 24 cupcake tins. Boil or steam the potatoes for 15 minutes, or until tender. Drain well, reserving the cooking liquid. Return the potatoes to the pan and mash until smooth. Set aside 1 cup (230 g) mashed potato for the pastry. Add the canola oil to the remaining potato and beat with a wooden spoon until smooth and creamy, adding a little of the reserved cooking liquid if necessary. You will need about 2 cups (460 g) creamed mashed potato for the topping.

For the pastry, scoop the reserved warm mashed potato into a large bowl. Stir in the extra oil. Add the sifted flour and baking powder and the salt. Using your hands, knead the dough into a smooth ball, adding enough egg to combine. (Reserve the remaining egg for glazing.) Place on a lightly floured board and knead lightly. Roll out the pastry and, using a 2½–3 in (6–7 cm) cutter, cut out rounds. Divide among the prepared tins. Bake for 5 minutes. Cool.

For the filling, heat the oil in a frying pan and cook the meat until lightly browned and cooked through. Add the stock and simmer for 5 minutes. Remove from the heat. Add the blended cornstarch and stir until combined. Return to the heat, stirring continuously until the mixture boils and thickens. Add salt and parsley. Cool before using.

Place a tablespoon of cooled meat mixture into each pastry case. Spoon or pipe the reserved creamed mashed potato on top, making sure the top is completely covered with potato. Brush with reserved egg. Bake for 10 minutes, or until the pastry is cooked and the potato is golden brown. Serve at once.

HINT: If you want to make these in advance, the pastry cases can be made, partially cooked and frozen. Thaw at room temperature, fill, top and bake.

sausage rolls

Low chemical.
Free of egg, dairy, gluten, nut and soy.

canola oil, for greasing

14 oz (400 g) white-skinned
potatoes, peeled and
roughly chopped

1 tablespoon canola oil

1 cup (150 g) soy-free,
gluten-free self-raising flour

½ teaspoon gluten-free
baking powder

½ teaspoon ground sea salt

1 egg, or equivalent
egg substitute

FILLING

10½ oz (300 g) ground
(minced) chicken or veal

1 egg, or equivalent
egg substitute

½ cup (40 g) gluten-free fresh
breadcrumbs

1 scallion (spring onion),
finely chopped

½ teaspoon ground sea salt

1 tablespoon water

1 egg, or equivalent egg
substitute, extra

Prep time: 45 minutes

Cooking time: 25 minutes

Makes 20–24 rolls

Preheat the oven to 400°F (200°C/Gas 6). Lightly grease two baking trays. Boil or steam the potatoes for 15 minutes, or until tender. Drain well. Return the potatoes to the pan and mash until smooth. You will need 1 cup (230 g) mashed potato for this recipe.

Combine the mashed potato and oil in a large bowl. Add the sifted dry ingredients and enough egg to mix to a smooth dough. (Reserve the remaining egg for glazing.) Knead on a lightly floured board until smooth. Roll the dough out on a lightly floured surface into a 14 in (35 cm) square, trimming the edges. Cut the dough into three strips.

For the filling, combine the meat, egg, breadcrumbs, scallion and salt in a bowl, add the water and mix well to combine. Divide the filling into three portions and, using wet hands, form each portion into thin rolls. Lay the filling along the center of the pastry strips and brush extra egg along the edges. Wrap the pastry around the filling with the seam side down. Repeat with the remaining filling and pastry.

Brush the rolls with the remaining egg, then cut each roll into six pieces. Place the sausage rolls on the prepared trays, prick the tops with a fork and bake for 20–25 minutes, or until cooked through and lightly browned.

HINTS: Sausage rolls can be made a day in advance and kept in the refrigerator. When required, wrap the cooked sausage rolls in aluminium foil and reheat at 350°F (180°C/Gas 4) for 5–8 minutes. If you can tolerate gluten, you can use store bought puff pastry with no added preservatives or antioxidants, instead of potato pastry.

honeycomb

Low chemical.
Free of egg, dairy, gluten, nut and soy.

⅓ cup (55 g) sugar
2 tablespoons golden syrup
2 teaspoons water
1 teaspoon baking soda
(bicarbonate of soda)

Prep time: 15 minutes
Cooking time: 10 minutes
Serves 4–6

Lightly grease an 11 x 7 in (28 x 18 cm) tin. Put the sugar, golden syrup and water in a large saucepan over low heat. Stir until the sugar is dissolved. Bring to a boil and boil for 7 minutes.

Remove from the heat and quickly add the baking soda. Stir quickly and pour into the prepared tin. Do not move the tin while the honeycomb is setting.

Mark into pieces while still warm or break into pieces when completely set. Store in an airtight container.

Some foods can cause a range of symptoms in certain children, such as behavior disturbances, hyperactivity, hives, mouth ulcers, headaches, limb pains, abdominal pains, or flu-like symptoms. The tendency to food chemical intolerance runs in families.

carob-coated honeycomb

Low chemical.
Contains dairy and soy. Free of egg, gluten and nut.

Place 1 cup (160 g) carob chips and 2 tablespoons canola oil in a heatproof bowl over a saucepan of simmering water. Heat until the carob is melted. Stir gently to combine. Do not overheat as it will become very thick. Spread over the honeycomb when completely set. Allow the carob to set—you can do this in the refrigerator but don't permanently store the honeycomb in the fridge. Cut or break into pieces. (Remember to check whether the carob chips contain soy and/or dairy.)

marshmallows

Low chemical.
Free of egg, dairy, gluten, nut and soy.

⅓ cup (50 g) powdered gelatine

1 cup (250 ml) cold water

4 cups (880 g) sugar

2 cups (500 ml) boiling water

1 cup (125 g) pure confectioners' (icing) sugar

½ cup (60 g) maize cornstarch (cornflour)

Prep time: 25 minutes + setting time
Cooking time: 20 minutes
Makes 32 squares

Sprinkle the gelatine over the cold water and set aside.

Put the sugar and boiling water in a large saucepan. Stir over low heat until the sugar is dissolved. Add the gelatine mixture. Stir until well combined and dissolved. Boil steadily without a lid for 15 minutes. Remove from the heat and allow to cool until lukewarm.

Pour the mixture into the large bowl of an electric mixer. Beat on high speed until white and thick. Pour into two wet 8 in (20 cm) square deep cake tins. Refrigerate for 1–2 hours, or preferably overnight, until set.

Sift the confectioners' sugar and cornstarch together into a bowl. Cut the marshmallow into squares using a large wet knife. Remove from the tins and toss in the combined confectioners' sugar and cornstarch. Store the marshmallows in layers, separating each layer with a sheet of waxed paper or baking paper. Ensure each marshmallow is well coated with the confectioners' sugar and cornstarch mixture to avoid sticking together.

carob-coated marshmallows

Low chemical.
Contains dairy and soy. Free of egg, gluten and nut.

Combine 1 cup (160 g) carob chips and 2 tablespoons canola oil in a heatproof bowl. Place over a saucepan of simmering water until the carob is melted. Stir to combine. Do not overheat as it will become very thick. Drizzle over or dip in squares of marshmallow. All carob chips contain some dairy and many also contain soy.

rocky road

Low chemical.
Contains nuts, dairy and soy. Free of egg and gluten.

2 tablespoons powdered gelatine

½ cup (125 ml) cold water

2 cups (440 g) sugar

1 cup (250 ml) boiling water

½ cup (60 g) pure confectioners' (icing) sugar

¼ cup (30 g) maize cornstarch (cornflour)

⅓ cup (50 g) chopped cashews

1½ cups (240 g) carob chips

¼ cup (60 ml) canola oil

Prep time: 45 minutes + setting time
Cooking time: 35 minutes
Makes 48 pieces

Sprinkle the gelatine over the cold water and set aside.

Put the sugar and boiling water in a large pan. Stir over low heat until sugar is dissolved. Add the gelatine mixture. Stir until well combined and dissolved. Boil steadily without a lid for 15 minutes. Remove from the heat and allow to cool until lukewarm.

Pour the mixture into the large bowl of an electric mixer. Beat on high speed until white and thick. Pour into a wet 8 x 12 in (20 x 30 cm) baking tin. Refrigerate for 1–2 hours, or preferably overnight, until set.

Sift the confectioners' sugar and cornstarch together into a bowl. Cut the marshmallow into 1 in (2.5 cm) squares using a large wet knife. Remove from the tin and toss in the combined confectioners' sugar and cornstarch.

Lightly grease an 8 x 12 in (20 x 30 cm) baking tin. Put the marshmallow pieces into the tin and sprinkle with the chopped cashews.

Melt the carob and oil in a heatproof bowl over a saucepan of simmering water. Stir gently to combine. Do not overheat as it will become very thick. Cool slightly.

Pour the melted carob over the marshmallows and chopped cashews. Allow to set in the refrigerator. Cut into squares.

HINT: Check whether your carob chips contain dairy and/or soy.

Although gelatine contains sulphite (220) as a preservative, it is removed when the gelatine is boiled.

cupcakes

Low chemical.
Free of egg, dairy, gluten, nut and soy.

4½ oz (125 g) dairy-free margarine

½ cup (125 g) superfine (caster) sugar

2 eggs, or equivalent egg substitute

1 cup (150 g) soy-free, gluten-free self-raising flour

½ cup (90 g) rice flour

3 teaspoons gluten-free baking powder

½ cup (125 ml) rice milk

pure confectioners' (icing) sugar, for dusting

Prep time: 15 minutes
Cooking time: 20 minutes
Makes 24

Preheat the oven to 350°F (180°C/Gas 4). Line two 12-cup ⅓ cup (80 ml) muffin holes or muffin tins with paper liners.

In the small bowl of an electric mixer, beat the margarine and sugar together until light and fluffy. Add the eggs, one at a time, beating well after each addition.

Sift the dry ingredients into a large bowl. Fold the dry ingredients into the margarine mixture alternately with the rice milk.

Spoon the mixture evenly into the muffin holes and bake for about 15–20 minutes, or until just cooked.

Dust the cupcakes with confectioners' sugar.

HINT: These cupcakes can also be iced with carob icing (see page 226). If desired, they can be frozen, iced or un-iced, in lots of six for convenience. Thaw out at room temperature.

To hyperactive children, the natural chemicals in so-called healthy foods can be just as much of a problem as artificial additives. In sensitive children adverse effects are dose-related and can build up over a period, especially when eaten with many other different foods.

butter cakes with carob icing

Low chemical.
Contains egg, dairy and gluten. Free of nut and soy.

4½ oz (125 g) butter

½ cup (125 g) superfine (caster) sugar

2 eggs, lightly beaten

1½ cups (185 g) self-raising flour

½ cup (125 ml) milk

CAROB GLACÉ ICING

1½ cups (185 g) pure confectioners' (icing) sugar, sifted

1 tablespoon carob powder

Prep time: 15 minutes
Cooking time: 20 minutes
Makes 24 cupcakes

Preheat the oven to 350°F (180°C/Gas 4). Line two 12-cup 2 x ¾ in (5 x 2 cm) tart cases or ⅓ cup (80 ml) muffin holes with paper liners.

In the small bowl of an electric mixer, beat the butter and sugar until the mixture is light and fluffy. Add the eggs, one at a time, beating well after each addition.

Sift the flour into a large bowl. Fold the flour into the butter mixture alternately with the milk.

Spoon the mixture evenly into the tart cases and bake for about 15–20 minutes, or until just cooked.

To make the icing, combine the confectioners' sugar and carob powder in a heatproof bowl. Add enough cold water to make a stiff paste. Place the bowl over a saucepan of simmering water and stir continuously until the icing softens to the required consistency.

Use a small palette knife to spread the icing over these mini cakes. Decorate as desired.

HINT: The cooked cakes can simply be dusted with pure confectioners' (icing) sugar, if preferred.

birthday cake

Low chemical.
Contains egg. Free of dairy, gluten, nut and soy.

canola oil, for greasing

maize cornstarch (cornflour), for dusting

6 eggs

1 cup (220 g) sugar

⅓ cup (35 g) arrowroot

⅓ cup (40 g) maize cornstarch (cornflour)

½ cup (160 g) Pear Jam (see Basics)

MARSHMALLOW FROSTING

3 teaspoons powdered gelatine

1¾ cups (435 ml) boiling water

2¼ cups (500 g) sugar

Prep time: 1½ hours

Cooking time: 45 minutes

Makes 1 cake

Preheat the oven to 350°F (180°C/Gas 4). Lightly grease three 9 in (23 cm) shallow round tins or two 11 x 7 in (28 x 18 cm) tins, then dust with maize cornstarch.

Combine the eggs and sugar in the bowl of an electric mixer. Beat until thick and light. Gently fold in the sifted arrowroot and cornstarch. Divide mixture among the three round tins or two rectangular tins.

Bake for 25–30 minutes, or until well risen and pale golden. Turn onto wire racks to cool.

Sandwich the cooled cakes together using pear jam. Place the cake on a stiff board or plate.

For the marshmallow frosting, dissolve the gelatine in half of the boiling water. Pour into a saucepan. Add the remainder of the water and the sugar and mix well. Heat gently, stirring until boiling. Simmer without stirring over low heat for 15 minutes.

Remove the pan from the heat and allow to cool slightly. Scoop the frosting into the large bowl of an electric mixer and beat on high speed until the mixture doubles in bulk and becomes thick. Spread quickly over the cake, using a metal spatula.

HINT: The sponge cake can be made and frozen, un-iced. Put in a container to freeze to ensure the cake keeps its shape. Thaw at room temperature and ice. The cake can be iced and decorated up to 12 hours before the party.

marshmallow teddy bear cake

Low chemical.
Free of egg, dairy, gluten, nut and soy.

⅓ cup (50 g) powdered gelatine

1 cup (250 ml) cold water

4 cups (880 g) sugar

2 cups (500 ml) boiling water

¼ teaspoon citric acid

2 teaspoons natural vanilla extract

DECORATION

maize cornstarch (cornflour), for dusting

⅓ cup (40 g) maize cornstarch (cornflour)

1 heaping tablespoon pure confectioners' (icing) sugar

½ cup (5 g) puffed rice cereal

1 teaspoon carob powder

2 tablespoons pure confectioners' (icing) sugar, extra

Prep time: 25 minutes + setting time
Cooking time: 20 minutes
Makes 1 cake

Sprinkle the gelatine over the cold water and set aside.

Put the sugar and boiling water in a large saucepan. Stir over low heat until the sugar is dissolved. Add the gelatine mixture. Stir until well combined and dissolved. Boil steadily, uncovered, for 15 minutes. Let cool until lukewarm. Add the citric acid and vanilla.

Pour the mixture into the large bowl of an electric mixer. Beat on high speed until white and thick.

Meanwhile, soak a teddy bear cake mold in the sink with ice cubes for about 5 minutes. Remove from the sink without drying. Pour the marshmallow mixture into the teddy bear mold. Refrigerate for 1–2 hours, or preferably overnight, until set.

Sprinkle the top of the cake with cornstarch, then run around the edge of the mold with a knife dipped in hot water. Slowly and carefully ease the marshmallow out of the mold onto a cake board—you may need to use a spatula to ease the marshmallow out.

Sift together the cornstarch and confectioners' sugar, then sprinkle over the cake. Put the puffed rice cereal in a plastic bag, then run a rolling pin over the top to crush the cereal. Use the crushed cereal to make the pattern for the bear's ears, paws, snout and belly.

To make the icing, mix the carob powder and extra confectioners' sugar together, then add a few drops of water until you have a spreadable consistency. Spoon into a piping bag, then pipe on the eyes, nose and mouth. Decorate with a ribbon, if desired.

HINT: Look in kitchenware or department stores to find other fun molds.

lemon cordial

Low chemical.
Free of egg, dairy, gluten, nut and soy.

2 cups (440 g) sugar
2 cups (500 ml) water
1 teaspoon citric acid

Prep time: 5 minutes
Cooking time: 15 minutes
Makes 3 cups (750 ml)

Place the sugar and water in a saucepan. Stir over low heat until the sugar dissolves. Add the citric acid and stir to combine. Remove from the heat. Place in a sealed container and store in the refrigerator.

Pour a small amount into a tall chilled glass and top with chilled soda, mineral or tap water. Stir lightly to distribute the cordial evenly.

HINT: For a special occasion, serve cordial in a frosted glass. Dip the rim of the glass in lightly beaten egg white. Dip immediately into crystal sugar. Allow to dry before using. For a stronger lemon flavor, add an extra ½–1 teaspoon citric acid.

lemon popsicles

Low chemical.
Free of egg, dairy, gluten, nut and soy.

Use the diluted lemon cordial to make lemon popsicles (iceblocks). Simply pour into plastic molds and freeze, or freeze in ice cube trays for adding to drinks.

vanilla milkshake

Low chemical.
Contains dairy. Free of egg, gluten, nut and soy.

2 cups (500 ml) milk,
well chilled

1 teaspoon natural
vanilla extract

sugar, to taste

Combine the milk, vanilla and sugar. Whisk, beat or blend together. Pour into long glasses to serve.

HINT: Milkshakes can be made using an electric blender, a whisk, or a rotary beater, or the ingredients can be placed in a tall sealed container and shaken until frothy.

Prep time: 5 minutes
Cooking time: Nil
Serves 2

carob milkshake

Low chemical.
Contains dairy. Free of egg, gluten, nut and soy.

1 tablespoon carob powder

1 tablespoon sugar

1 tablespoon hot water

2 cups (500 ml) milk,
well chilled

¼ cup (40 g) finely chopped
carob chips

Dissolve the carob powder and sugar in hot water. Allow to cool.

Combine the milk and carob mixture. Whisk, beat or blend together. Pour into long glasses. Top with finely chopped carob chips.

HINT: Ask your health food store whether their carob chips contain dairy and/or soy.

Prep time: 5 minutes
Cooking time: Nil
Serves 2

pear slushy

Low chemical.
Free of egg, dairy, gluten, nut and soy.

1 lb 13 oz (825 g) can pear
halves in syrup

1 teaspoon citric acid

Prep time: 15 minutes +
freezing
Cooking time: Nil
Serves 4–6

Put the pears, syrup and citric acid into an electric blender. Blend on high for 2–3 minutes.

Pour into a shallow metal tin and freeze for about 1 hour, or until just frozen around the edges. Scrape this ice back into the mixture with a fork. Repeat every 30 minutes until the mixture has even-sized ice crystals. Serve immediately or beat with a fork and refreeze until just before serving. Allow to soften slightly in the refrigerator before using. The mixture should be slushy.

Pile into tall chilled glasses and serve with a spoon and a straw.

mango juice

Moderate chemical.
Free of egg, dairy, gluten, nut and soy.

3 cups (555 g) fresh
mango, peeled

¼ cup (55 g) sugar

½ cup (125 ml) water

Prep time: 5 minutes
Cooking time: Nil
Serves 4–6

Blend the mango flesh with the sugar and water in a blender on high for 2–3 minutes, or until puréed.

Dilute as desired to serve.

HINT: If fresh mangoes aren't in season, use 1 lb 8 oz (675 g) canned mangoes in syrup and blend to a purée (3 cups, including syrup)—you won't need any extra sugar or water. Dilute as desired.

With a few basics on hand, you'll always be ready to add extra flavor to meals without the risk of reactions to food chemicals. Low chemical stocks can be prepared ahead and stored in the freezer. Pear chutney makes a great pantry standby—it can even be puréed for an instant sauce to serve with cold meat. And homemade mayonnaise and salad dressing put an end to dull salads.

basics

pear juice

Low chemical.
Free of egg, dairy, gluten, nut and soy.

1 lb 13 oz (825 g) can pear halves in syrup

Put the pears and syrup into an electric blender. Blend on high speed for 2–3 minutes, or until puréed.

Prep time: 5 minutes
Cooking time: Nil
Serves 4–6

Scoop into a covered container and refrigerate. Store for 3–4 days.

HINT: Pear juice may be diluted with soda, unflavored mineral water or tap water. Use as a drink, or whenever a recipe calls for pear juice.

pear chutney

Low chemical.
Free of egg, dairy, gluten, nut and soy.

1 lb 13 oz (825 g) can pear halves in syrup

½ cup firmly packed (115 g) soft brown sugar

1½ teaspoons citric acid

1 teaspoon ground sea salt

Prep time: 10 minutes
Cooking time: 25 minutes
Makes 1½ cups

Drain and chop the pears, reserving the syrup.

Pour the syrup into a saucepan. Bring to a boil and boil until the mixture is reduced by half.

Add the pears, sugar, citric acid and salt. Reduce the heat. Allow to simmer for about 10–15 minutes, or until the mixture is thick.

Spoon into hot, sterilized jars. Seal, label and date. Once opened, store in the refrigerator and use within 3 weeks.

pear jam

Low chemical.
Free of egg, dairy, gluten, nut and soy.

1 lb 10 oz (750 g) ripe, peeled pears, or 2 x 1 lb 13 oz (825 g) cans of pears, drained

1 lb 10 oz (750 g) white sugar

1 x 1¾ oz (50 g) package jam setting mixture

Prep time: 10 minutes
Cooking time: 10 minutes
Makes about 2⅓ cups

Purée the pears in a blender or food processor. Scoop the purée into a large saucepan and heat over medium heat. Stir in the sugar and jam setting mixture. Reduce the heat to low and stir until the sugar is dissolved. Increase the heat and bring to a boil. Boil for 5 minutes, stirring occasionally. Remove from the heat.

Allow to cool for 10 minutes, then pour into sterilized jars. Seal, label and date. Once opened, store in the refrigerator and use within 4 weeks.

HINT: Use as a spread, filling or topping.

vegetable stock

Low chemical.
Free of egg, dairy, gluten, nut and soy.

1 tablespoon canola oil

3 celery stalks, sliced

12 oz (350 g) rutabaga (swede), peeled and chopped

1 large leek, halved lengthways, washed and chopped

3 garlic cloves, crushed

4.5 liters (18 cups) water

ground sea salt

Prep time: 15 minutes

Cooking time: 1¾ hours

Makes about 10 cups

Heat the oil in a large saucepan or stockpot over medium heat. Add the celery, rutabaga, leek and garlic. Cook, stirring often, for 5–8 minutes or until the vegetables turn light golden. Pour in the water. Cover with a lid and bring to a boil. Simmer, partially covered, for 1½ hours, or until the vegetables are very soft.

Strain the stock. Season with salt to taste. Set aside to cool, then transfer to an airtight container. Use the stock on the day of making or freeze for up to 4 weeks.

chicken or veal stock

Low chemical.
Free of egg, dairy, gluten, nut and soy.

Put 1 lb 2 oz (500 g) chicken or veal bones in a large heavy-based saucepan. Add 1 leek and 1 celery stalk, both roughly chopped, and 4 parsley stalks (without foliage). Cover with water and bring to a boil, skimming the surface. Reduce the heat and simmer for 1–1½ hours, uncovered. Strain through a colander, then through a fine sieve. Season with salt and refrigerate. Remove any fat from the surface. Use on the day of making or freeze for up to 4 weeks. Makes 2–2½ cups.

stock with carrot

Moderate chemical.
Free of egg, dairy, gluten, nut and soy.

For the less sensitive, you can increase the flavor of either of the stock recipes by adding 1 roughly chopped carrot.

mayonnaise

Low chemical.
Contains egg. Free of dairy, gluten, nut and soy.

2 egg yolks
¼ teaspoon ground sea salt
1 cup (250 ml) canola oil
¼ teaspoon citric acid

Prep time: 20 minutes
Cooking time: Nil
Makes 1 cup

Put the egg yolks and salt in a bowl and whisk together until well combined and thick.

Gradually whisk in the oil, drop by drop, from a teaspoon until a quarter of the oil has been added. The mixture should be thick at this stage. Very slowly pour in the remaining oil in a thick steady stream, while continuing to beat steadily. Beat in the citric acid. Store the mayonnaise in a glass jar in the refrigerator for up to 3 days.

HINT: Mayonnaise can be made in a blender or food processor. Use the same ingredients as above. Blend the eggs and salt for a few seconds. With the motor running, pour in the oil in a steady thin stream. When all the oil has been added, the mixture should be thick.

salad dressing

Low chemical.
Free of egg, dairy, gluten, nut and soy.

1 teaspoon citric acid
2 teaspoons hot water
½ cup (125 ml) canola oil
½ cup (125 ml) Pear Juice
(see page 236)
ground sea salt

Prep time: 5 minutes
Cooking time: Nil
Makes 1 cup

Dissolve the citric acid in the hot water. Combine the oil, juice, citric acid solution and salt. Mix well to combine. Pour into a glass jar or bottle. Store in the refrigerator for up to 3 days.

HINT: Equal quantities of oil and pear juice have been used. Adjust proportions to taste.

This chapter will help you to choose the foods that are best for you. It contains lists of low chemical foods from all the main food groups as well as useful summaries of the things to avoid. There is also a handy table of the food additives that are most likely to cause adverse reactions. And lastly, all the recipes are grouped into sections so you can see at a glance what will suit your particular dietary needs.

useful information

shopping list

This is a general and comprehensive list. When consulting it, you should bear in mind your own intolerances and/or allergies, and avoid particular foods as necessary. Nut products should be strictly avoided by those with an allergy to any kind of nut.

cereals, grains & flours

GLUTEN-FREE
Rice, white and brown
Rice cakes, plain
Rice cereals: Rolled, flakes
Rice bran
Rice flour
Rice noodles, vermicelli
Rice pasta
Rice bread
Maize cornstarch (cornflour)
Arrowroot
Buckwheat
Buckwheat flour
Millet
Potato flour
Sago
Tapioca
Amaranth

CONTAINS GLUTEN
Wheat
Wheat bran
Wheat cornstarch
    (cornflour)
Wheat flour
Plain wheat pasta
Barley
Malt rye
Rye flour
Rolled oats
Oat bran
Oat cereals, plain
Baby cereals, plain

Avoid: *Fragrant or scented rice (Basmati or jasmine); wild rice; flavored rice cakes (corn or sesame); all corn products (maize flour, cornmeal, polenta, corn cereals, flaked corn crumbs and corn bread); colored or flavored noodles; canned spaghetti; non-plain breakfast cereals (with corn, dried fruit, coconut, honey, nuts, flavors or colors); rice baby cereals.*

breads

Bread: White, whole wheat
Bread rolls
Pita bread, plain, unpreserved

Avoid: *Wholegrain or multigrain; breads containing corn, dried fruits, vinegar, preservatives, mold inhibitors, propianates (280–283); crumpets (282); muffins (282, 202); pita bread (282); bread improver (220–228).*

fruits

Pears: Soft and ripe
Canned pears in
    sugar syrup
Baby pears

Avoid: *All other fresh fruits; canned fruit in natural juice or nectar (including pears); fruit jellies; fruit juices; all dried fruits; nashi pears.*

vegetables (fresh or frozen)

Potatoes: Brown
    or large white
Chayote (choko)
Rutabaga (swedes)
Brussels sprouts
Cabbage
Celery
Lettuce: Iceberg
Green beans: French, string
Bean shoots
Mung bean sprouts
Bamboo shoots
Leeks
Scallions (spring onions)
Chives
Garlic
Canned or dried legumes:
    Lentils, soy beans, split
    peas, bean mix

Avoid: *All other vegetables; red potatoes; new potatoes; instant mashed potato (220); store bought potato chips; turnips; Chinese vegetables; other lettuce varieties; fava (broad) beans; dehydrated peas (220, 221); alfalfa; onions; pickled vegetables; canned baked beans; bean mixes with added flavors; canned soups; dried instant soups; baby food in jars or cans; green peas.*

meats, chicken & fish

Fresh beef
Veal
Lamb
Rabbit
Chicken, skinless
Fish, fresh white
Fresh crab and lobster
Calamari
Scallops

Avoid: *Aged beef; corned beef; sausage rolls; meat pies; frankfurts; sausages; processed sandwich meats; salami; meat paste; beef stock or bouillon; offal; gravy; chicken and duck liver patés; pressed chicken; self-basting turkey; pork and pork products; bacon; ham; prawns (shrimp); salmon; tuna; frozen fish; canned fish; salted fish; smoked fish; fish sauces and marinades; fish pastes.*

eggs

Fresh eggs
Frozen egg white mix
Egg substitute

Avoid: *custard powder (102, 107, 110, 160B).*

dairy products (cow or goat)

Butter: Salted, unsalted
Ghee
Cream: Fresh, sour, reduced, thickened
Milk, plain, unflavored: Fresh, full cream, low fat, skim, buttermilk, UHT, condensed, powdered, evaporated
Milk, flavored: With permitted ingredients
Yogurt: Plain, vanilla
Ice cream: Vanilla, no color
Fresh cheese: Cream cheese, mascarpone, ricotta, farm, cottage

Avoid: *Flavored butters; artificial creams; flavored or colored milk, yogurt or ice cream; store bought custards; gelato; cheese slices; cottage cheese in tubs (plain or flavored, 200–203); all other cheeses.*

soy products

Soy milk: Plain, vanilla, carob

Soy yogurt: Plain, vanilla
Soy custard: Plain, vanilla
Soy cream cheese
Tofu
Tofu ice cream, vanilla

Avoid: *Soy sauce; miso; tempeh; tamari; soy cheese.*

drinks

Plain milk: Cow, goat, sheep
Malted milk powder
Soy milk: Plain, vanilla, carob
Rice milk: Plain, vanilla, carob
Bottled lemon lime soda (lemonade), preservative-free
Bottled tonic water, preservative-free
Water: Unflavored spring, mineral or soda
Decaffeinated coffee
Alcohol: Gin, vodka, whisky

Avoid: *Chocolate flavoring for milks; cocoa; cola drinks; cordials; effervescent powders; flavored mineral water; flavored syrups; fruit flavored powders; fruit juices; fruit syrups; sodas (soft drinks); tomato juice; vegetable juice; coffee; coffee substitutes; tea; fruit/herbal teas; decaffeinated teas; beer; cider; rum; port; brandy; sherry; liqueurs; wine.*

margarine & oils

Margarine: Sunflower, soy, safflower, canola (no antioxidant)
Margarine, milk-free
Oil: Canola, soy, sunflower, safflower (no antioxidant)

Avoid: *Margarines with preservative (sorbate 200–203) or color (annatto 160B); coconut cream/milk; all other oils; antioxidant (310–312, 319–321); store bought salad dressings/mayonnaise.*

baking aids, herbs, spices & condiments

Salt: Sea, rock, table
Baking powder
Baking soda (bicarbonate of soda) (500)
Citric acid (330)
Cream of tartar (334)
Gelatine (boiling will remove 220)
Natural vanilla extract
Baker's yeast
Poppy seeds
Parsley (sprinkle only)
Saffron
Jam setting mixture

Avoid: *Flavored salts; flavoring extracts; syrups; food colors; fresh herbs (except chives and a sprinkle of parsley); dried herbs; dried fruit; spices;*

pepper; chillies; onion; all bouillon cubes; meat extracts; yeast extracts; store bought sauces/marinades; gravies; tomato ketchup (sauce); tomato paste; vinegar; pickles.

jams, spreads, sugars & sweets

Sugar: White, brown, pure confectioners' (icing), superfine (caster)
Rice syrup
Golden syrup
Maple syrup, pure
Malt extract
Carob: Chips, powder
Store bought sweets: White jelly beans, white marshmallows, plain caramels, toffee

Avoid: *Raw sugar; molasses; treacle; honey; maple-flavored syrup (202); jams; conserves; jellies; lemon curd (butter); lemon spread; peanut butter; peanut paste; roasted cashew nut paste; other nut pastes; sesame paste; yeast extracts; chocolate; chocolate flavors; flavored/colored sweets; chewing gum; liquorice; mints; peppermints; flavored/colored popsicles or iced confections.*

crackers, cookies & cakes

Plain rice cakes
Plain water crackers
Plain crispbread
Plain sweet cookies
Shortbread, plain (no color)

Avoid: *Flavored rice cakes/snacks; store bought cakes/pastries (with cream, chocolate, fruit, nuts, jam, spices, color, preservative); Christmas cake/fruitcake; store bought griddle cakes; pancakes (with colors and/or preservatives); flavored crackers, cookies and crispbreads.*

nuts, chips & snacks

Raw cashews
Potato chips, plain
Lightly roasted cashew
nut paste

Avoid: *All other nuts; flavored potato chips; corn chips; tacos; store bought hot chips; flavored snack foods (fruit, honey, nuts, coconut, cheese, herbs, spices (621)).*

toiletries

Unflavored toothpaste
Soaps, shampoos,
conditioners,
moisturizers: Plain, only
lightly perfumed

Deodorants, unscented:
Roll-on, stick
Sunscreen, PABA-free
Laundry detergents,
soap powders:
Unscented

Avoid: *Flavored/ colored toothpaste; mouthwashes; strongly perfumed products; perfumes; after-shave lotions; aerosol deodorants; hair sprays; sunscreens with PABA; all fabric conditioners; washing and ironing sprays.*

medications, vitamins & minerals

Pain relief: Paracetamol,
codeine
Local anaesthetic: Plain
xylocaine (with no
preservative)
Antacid tablets/powders:
No color/flavor
Vitamins: No PABA, herbs,
color or flavor
Calcium: No color/flavor
Iron: No color/flavor

Avoid: *All non-essential medications; colored tablets and capsules (colors can be washed off tablets and capsules can be opened and emptied onto a spoon); syrups; mixtures; liquid preparations (colored, flavored, preserved); all aspirin preparations; children's paracetamol syrups, including color-free local anaesthetics with preservatives; menthol, eucalyptus oil; oil of wintergreen; cough syrups and lozenges; all non-steroidal anti-inflammatory drugs; vitamins with PABA; liquid/flavored vitamins; 'megadose' vitamins; flavored/colored calcium preparations; all herbal remedies; incense/massage oils; all aromatherapy and/or essential oils.*

FOOD ADDITIVES

CODE NUMBERS OF ADDITIVES MOST LIKELY TO CAUSE ADVERSE REACTIONS

Colors	
Artificial	102, 107, 110, 122–129, 132, 133, 142, 151, 155
Natural	160B (annatto)

Preservatives	
Sorbates	200–203
Benzoates	210–218
Sulphites	220–228
Nitrates, nitrites	249–252
Propionates	280–283
Antioxidants	310–312, 319–321

Flavor enhancers	
Glutamate (e.g. MSG)	620–635
Hydrolyzed vegetable protein (HVP)	
Textured vegetable protein (TVP)	

Most other additives are unlikely to cause adverse reactions. Anti-caking agents, bleaches, emulsifiers, mineral salts, propellants, food acids, thickening agents, sweeteners, vegetable gums and vitamins are generally safe, even for food sensitive people.

For more information about food intolerances and allergy, as well as dietary and lifestyle tips and more recipes, see http://www.cs.nsw.gov.au/rpa/allergy/

recipe list

MODERATE CHEMICAL

WHEAT-FREE & GLUTEN-FREE

DAIRY-FREE

EGG-FREE

The recipe gives the option of using either egg or equivalent egg substitute. For egg-free diets, use egg substitute.

Sausage rolls* 219
Savory flat bread 147
Scallion and cheese
    scones 173
Soy cashew
    loaf* 117
Spring rolls 55
Spring salad 76
Spring salad with cashew
    nut dressing 76
Sprout and cabbage
    salad 132

Steamed jam pudding* 193
Stock with carrot 238
Sugar-glazed potato 124
Sugar-glazed sweet
    potato 124
Tamarillo sorbet 194
Tangy baked chicken and
    rice 93
Tangy yogurt sauce 104
Toasted wheat-free
    muesli 31
Traditional scones 173

Tropical frozen
    yogurt 196
Tropical ice cream 192
Vanilla cookies 162
Vanilla milkshake 231
Veal and chicken
    terrine* 65
Veal meatballs* 100
Veal rolls with leek
    sauce 97
Vegetable and veal
    pasta 99

Vegetable and veal pasta
    with carrot 99
Vegetable pouches* 66
Vegetable soup 69
Vegetable stock 238
Vegetable strudels 63
Vodka pear slushy 213
Warm quail salad 77
Wheat flour muffins* 36
Wheat-free muesli 31
Wheatless loaf 143
Whole wheat scones 173

NUT-FREE

Angel pear flan 199
Apple and cinnamon
    muffins 181
Apple bar cookie 161
Asian-style salad 79
Asparagus and cottage
    cheese pie 74
Asparagus and leek puffs 60
Baked beans 47
Baked butternut squash 105
Baked eggs in potato 44
Baked rutabaga 105
Banana and caramel
    tart 204
Banana loaf 178
Banana muffins 181
Birthday cake 227
Bread rolls 142
Breadcrumb-coated
    fish 102
Brown sugar cookies 162
Buckwheat pancakes 35
Butter cakes with carob
    icing 226

Butter pinwheels 165
Butter puffs with lamb 61
Butternut and breadcrumb
    stuffing 107
Butternut and coconut
    tart 168
Butternut and leek sauce 97
Butternut muffins 38
Butterscotch pudding 186
Buttery oat cookies 176
Caramelized beef and
    potatoes 110
Carob brownies 157
Carob-chip cookies 162
Carob-coated
    honeycomb 221
Carob-coated
    marshmallows 222
Carob mallow dessert 200
Carob meringue kisses 159
Carob milkshake 231
Carob self-saucing
    pudding 188
Carob topping 157

Carob truffles 208
Carob waffles 43
Carrot and potato
    purée 122
Cheese pinwheels 64
Cheesy egg and vegetable
    strudels 63
Cheesy fish pie 108
Chicken and carrot
    sausage 96
Chicken and leek puffs 58
Chicken and pasta salad 118
Chicken and vegetable
    pasta 86
Chicken or veal stock 238
Chicken with glazed
    pears 109
Chickpea dip 53
Chickpea fritters 113
Chinese-style chicken
    noodles 116
Chinese-style chicken and
    vegetables with
    noodles 116

Chunky rice bar cookie 153
Coffee-baked bananas 191
Coffee-baked pears 191
Coffee mousse meringue
    roll 164
Coffee slushy 212
Continental chicken
    sausage 96
Corn and chive muffins 36
Cream cheese truffles 208
Creamy potato salad 134
Creamy rice porridge 30
Creamy rutabaga purée 123
Crepes with two
    sauces 201
Crispy corn and potato
    bites 57
Crispy fish and lentils 91
Crispy poppy seed wafer
    crackers 56
Crispy potato bites 57
Crispy wafer crackers 56
Crumpets 41
Crunchy chicken bits 216

Sugar-glazed potato 124
Sugar-glazed sweet
potato 124
Sweet potato soufflé 131
Tamarillo sorbet 194
Tamarillos with gin
sabayon sauce 197
Tangy baked chicken and
rice 93
Tangy Greek-style sauce 100

Tangy yogurt sauce 104
Toasted wheat-free
muesli 31
Traditional banana loaf 178
Traditional butterscotch
pudding 186
Traditional carob
pudding 188
Traditional scones 173
Tropical frozen yogurt 196

Vanilla cookies 162
Vanilla milkshake 231
Veal and chicken
terrine 65
Veal meatballs 100
Veal rolls with leek
sauce 97
Vegetable and veal pasta 99
Vegetable and veal pasta
with carrot 99

Vegetable pouches 66
Vegetable soup 69
Vegetable stock 238
Vegetable strudels 63
Vodka pear slushy 213
Warm quail salad 77
Wheat flour muffins 36
Wheat-free muesli 31
Wheatless loaf 143
Whole wheat scones 173

EGG / DAIRY / GLUTEN / NUT - FREE

The recipe specifies both egg and equivalent egg substitute. For egg-free diets, use egg substitute.

Baked beans 47
Baked butternut squash 105
Baked rutabaga 105
Banana loaf * 178
Brown sugar cookies 162
Buckwheat pancakes* 35
Butternut and breadcrumb
stuffing 107
Butternut and leek sauce 97
Butternut muffins 38
Butterscotch pudding * 186
Caramelized beef and
potatoes 110
Carob self-saucing
pudding* (contains
soy) 188
Carrot and potato
purée 122
Chicken and carrot
sausage* 96
Chicken and leek puffs* 58
Chicken and vegetable
pasta 86
Chicken or veal stock 238

Chicken with glazed
pears 109
Chickpea dip 53
Chickpea fritters* 113
Chinese-style chicken
noodles* 116
Chinese-style chicken
and vegetables with
noodles* 116
Chunky rice bar cookie 153
Coffee-baked bananas 191
Coffee-baked pears 191
Coffee slushy 212
Continental chicken
sausage* 96
Corn and chive muffins* 36
Creamy rice porridge 30
Crepes with two
sauces* 201
Crispy corn and potato
bites* 57
Crispy fish and lentils 91
Crispy poppy seed wafer
crackers* 56

Crispy potato bites* 57
Crispy wafer crackers 56
Crunchy chicken bits* 216
Crunchy chicken bits with
chives* 216
Crunchy chicken bits with
garlic* 216
Cupcakes* 224
Fish and bean soup 73
Fish burgers 94
Fish pie 108
French-style potato
salad 134
French-style rice 135
Fresh spring rolls 55
Fried flat bread 148
Glazed chicken with garlic
and poppy seeds 81
Glazed drumsticks 81
Glazed lamb noisettes 92
Gluten-free apple bar
cookie* 160
Gluten-free banana
muffins* 180

Gluten-free bread rolls 140
Gluten-free butternut
scones 172
Gluten-free crumpets 39
Gluten-free herb
scones 172
Gluten-free pancakes* 34
Gluten-free pear bar
cookie* 160
Gluten-free pear
muffins* 180
Gluten-free rhubarb
muffins* 180
Gluten-free savory
corn and scallion
waffles* (contains
soy) 42
Gluten-free scones 172
Gluten-free steamed
pudding* 193
Gluten-free sweet carob
waffles* (contains
soy) 42
Gluten-free waffles* 42

This edition published by Barnes & Noble, Inc.,
by arrangement with Murdoch Books Pty Limited.

2004 Barnes & Noble Books

M 10 9 8 7 6 5 4 3 2 1

ISBN 0-7607-5892-1

Authors: Anne R Swain, MNutDiet, PhD; Velencia L Soutter, MBBS, FRACP; Robert H Loblay, MBBS, PhD, FRACP.

Project Manager: Zoë Harpham
Editorial Director: Diana Hill
Creative Director: Marylouise Brammer
Design Concept and Design: Susanne Geppert
Editor: Georgina Bitcon
US Editor: Justine Harding
Food Editor: Alison Roberts
Photographer: Ian Hofstetter
Stylist: Jane Collins
Food Preparation: Joanne Kelly
Recipes: Kerrie Carr, Kathy Knudsen, Alison Roberts, Kim Faulkner-Hogg.
Production: Monika Paratore

Printed by Toppan Hong Kong, CHINA.

© Text, design, photography and illustrations Murdoch Books/Royal Prince Alfred Hospital, Sydney 2004.
All rights reserved. No part of this publication may be reproduced, stored in a retrieval system or transmitted in any form or by any means, electronic, mechanical, photocopying, recording or otherwise without the prior written permission of the publisher.

IMPORTANT: Those who might be at risk from the effects of salmonella food poisoning (the elderly, pregnant women, young children and those suffering from immune deficiency diseases) should consult their doctor with any concerns about eating raw eggs.

CONVERSION GUIDE: You may find cooking times vary depending on the oven you are using. For fan-forced ovens, as a general rule, set the oven temperature to 70°F (20°C) lower than indicated in the recipe. We have used 4 teaspoon (20 ml) tablespoon measures. If you are using a 3 teaspoon (15 ml) tablespoon, for most recipes the difference will not be noticeable. However, for recipes using baking powder, gelatine, baking soda (bicarbonate of soda), small amounts of flour and cornstarch, add an extra teaspoon for each tablespoon specified.

The Publisher thanks Dinosaur Designs for the assistance in the photography of this book.
The Publisher acknowledges the contribution of Kim Faulkner-Hogg in the creation of the Sources of Gluten chart, page 13.